FATTY LIVER DIET COOKBOOK FOR NEWLY DIAGNOSED

Nourishing Your Way to Wellness with Flavorful Recipes and Essential Guidance for a Vibrant Life after a Fatty Liver Diagnosis

Smart Desty

Table of Contents:

Introduction

The term "fatty liver" has become increasingly common in the modern landscape of health awareness, catching attention due to its relationship with lifestyle and nutritional choices. Understanding the complexities of this disorder is the first step toward proactive management and reversal.

What Exactly is Fatty Liver?

Fatty liver, also known as hepatic steatosis, is a disorder in which excess fat accumulates in liver cells. Over time, this buildup can cause inflammation and impair liver function. Fatty liver disease is classified into two types: alcoholic fatty liver disease (AFLD) and non-alcoholic fatty liver disease (NAFLD). While AFLD is frequently connected with excessive alcohol intake, NAFLD is frequently associated with metabolic variables such as obesity, insulin resistance, and poor eating habits.

The Invisible Epidemic

Fatty liver disease, also known as the "silent epidemic," can proceed without obvious symptoms, making it difficult to diagnose in its early stages. However, when the disease progresses, symptoms such as weariness, stomach discomfort, and unexplained weight loss may appear. Fatty liver, if left untreated, can lead to more serious illnesses such as non-alcoholic steatohepatitis (NASH) and cirrhosis.

Tips for Beginners on Navigating Your Fatty Liver Journey

A Wellness Approach That Is Proactive

Receiving a fatty liver disease diagnosis can be both upsetting and inspiring. It is a call to action, pushing people to reconsider their lifestyles and make informed decisions to support liver health. This path necessitates a proactive strategy that includes not only dietary modifications but also lifestyle changes and a dedication to overall well-being.

How to Educate Yourself

Understanding the factors that contribute to fatty liver disease is an important step toward better health. Knowledge helps you to make informed decisions, whether it's about the influence of specific food choices, the function of insulin resistance, or the link between obesity and liver health. This cookbook is intended to be a great resource for deepening your understanding of fatty liver and guiding you on a culinary journey that promotes liver wellbeing.

The Value of Nutrition

Nutrition is critical in the management and even reversal of fatty liver disease. A nutrient-dense, whole-food diet promotes liver function, aids in weight management, and decreases inflammation. As you embark on this journey, the dishes supplied are painstakingly prepared to adhere to the principles of a fatty liver diet while also ensuring that each meal is a delectable culinary experience.

Developing Healthy Habits

Aside from dietary adjustments, developing healthy habits is critical for long-term success. Regular physical exercise, stress management, and enough sleep all contribute to general well-being and help to improve liver function. This cookbook goes beyond the kitchen, providing advice and insights on how to create a lifestyle that promotes good liver function.

The Cookbook's Function

This cookbook is a guide and companion for folks who have recently been diagnosed with fatty liver disease. It recognizes the difficulties of adopting a new food and lifestyle strategy and aims to make the transition as easy and enjoyable as possible. Each component is geared to provide full guidance for novices, from instructive chapters on fatty liver principles to practical pointers on navigating social settings and dining out.

Remember that you are not alone as you embark on this path. Numerous people have successfully treated and even corrected fatty liver disease by practicing mindful living and feeding their bodies the right meals. This cookbook is a tool for inspiring, educating, and empowering you to take charge of your health one delicious meal at a time.

You'll discover a professionally designed 30-day meal plan, complete with breakfasts, lunches, dinners, snacks, and desserts, on the following pages. Each recipe is beginner-friendly, so even those who are new to the world of mindful eating can reap the benefits of a fatty liver-friendly diet.

Allow this cookbook to be your culinary companion on your journey to liver fitness. May each dish not only fuel your body but also delight your taste buds, making your journey to a healthier, happier self a fulfilling and enjoyable experience.

Chapter 1: Fatty Liver Diet Fundamentals

What is the Fatty Liver Diet?

A "fatty liver diet" is a carefully curated dietary plan designed to support and promote liver function, specifically addressing the problems faced by fatty liver disease. This diet emphasizes nutrient-dense foods while restricting or avoiding those that promote liver inflammation and fat buildup.

The Fundamental Principles:

1. **Fat Consumption Moderation:** While it may appear contradictory, a fatty liver diet does not completely eliminate fats but instead emphasizes the consumption of healthy fats in moderation. This includes including omega-3 fatty acid sources, such as fish, flaxseeds, and walnuts, which are known for their anti-inflammatory qualities.

2. **Focus on Whole Foods:** A fatty liver diet emphasizes entire, unprocessed foods including fruits and vegetables, lean meats, and whole grains. These foods provide necessary nutrients while limiting the amount of sugar, preservatives, and artificial additives consumed.

3. **Carbohydrate Intake Control:** It is critical to control carbohydrate intake, particularly processed carbohydrates and sweets. This aids in the regulation of blood sugar levels and insulin resistance, which are both associated to the evolution of fatty liver disease.

4. **Sources of Lean Protein:** Protein is essential for liver health. In a fatty liver diet, lean protein sources such as poultry, fish, tofu, and legumes are preferable, as they promote muscle development and support metabolic activities.

5. **Alcohol Consumption Restriction:** Limiting or refraining from alcohol is critical for people with alcoholic fatty liver disease or those looking to enhance their liver function. Alcohol can worsen liver inflammation and contribute to further fat storage.

How Diet Affects Fatty Liver Health

The Root Cause: Excessive Fat Accumulation

The accumulation of fat within liver cells is the hallmark of fatty liver disease. Excess fat can cause inflammation, oxidative stress, and eventually impair liver function. Dietary variables, such as an excess of harmful fats and carbohydrates, are frequently the primary causes to excessive fat gain.

The Relationship Between Insulin Resistance and Sugar

High-refined-carbohydrate and sugar-containing diets contribute to insulin resistance, a condition in which cells become less sensitive to insulin. Insulin resistance not only contributes to the development and advancement of type 2 diabetes, but it also contributes to the development and progression of fatty liver disease. Sugar control is critical for regulating insulin resistance and supporting liver health.

Omega-6 Fatty Acids and Inflammation

When not balanced with anti-inflammatory omega-3 fatty acids, some dietary fats, notably omega-6 fatty acids present in processed oils and fried foods, can cause inflammation. Reducing your intake of omega-6-rich oils and replacing them with healthy fats helps to reduce inflammation and provides a protective layer for your liver.

The Effects of Alcohol on Liver Health

Excessive alcohol use directly adds to liver damage in the case of alcoholic fatty liver disease. Alcohol metabolism is prioritized by the liver, resulting in fat storage and inflammation. Eliminating or severely lowering alcohol consumption is critical for patients suffering from this type of fatty liver disease.

Essential Nutrients for Healthy Fatty Liver

1. Antioxidants are found in berries, citrus fruits, leafy greens, nuts, and seeds.

    Role: Antioxidants fight oxidative stress by decreasing inflammation and protecting liver cells.

2. Omega-3 Fatty Acids: Found in: Fatty fish (salmon, mackerel), flaxseeds, chia seeds, and walnuts.

    Omega-3 fatty acids support a healthy balance and prevent liver inflammation by counteracting the inflammatory effects of omega-6 fatty acids.

3. Fiber: Find it in whole grains, fruits, veggies, and legumes.

    Role: Fiber assists digestion, promotes gut health, and aids in weight management, all of which are necessary for good liver function.

4. Lean Proteins: - Found in poultry, fish, tofu, and lentils.

    Role: Tissue healing, muscle development, and metabolic support are all necessary without contributing to excessive fat buildup.

5. Vitamin E: Found in: Nuts, seeds, spinach, and broccoli.

    Role: Vitamin E is a potent antioxidant that protects liver cells from harm and promotes overall liver function.

As we progress through the cookbook, we'll notice that each recipe is designed with these concepts in mind, guaranteeing a balance of necessary nutrients to support your path toward a healthy liver. Understanding the fundamentals of a fatty liver diet allows you to make informed decisions that benefit the health of this crucial organ.

Chapter 2: Breakfast Delights
Recipe #1: Quinoa and Vegetable Breakfast Bowl

Start your day with a nutrient-rich breakfast dish that promotes a fatty liver diet. Quinoa contains important amino acids, and a variety of colorful veggies offer vitamins and minerals to improve liver function.

Ingredients:

- 1 cup washed quinoa.
- 2 cups water
- 1 tablespoon olive oil
- 1 red bell pepper, diced
- 1 zucchini, diced
- 1 cup halved cherry tomatoes
- 2 cups chopped spinach.
- Salt and pepper to taste.
- Poach 4 eggs.

4 servings.

Instructions:

1. 1: In a saucepan, mix quinoa and water. Bring to a boil, then decrease heat, cover, and simmer for 15-20 minutes, or until the quinoa is cooked and the water has been absorbed.
2. In a large pan, heat the olive oil over medium heat. Combine red bell pepper, zucchini, and cherry tomatoes. Sauté veggies until they are soft.
3. Mix in the chopped spinach and cooked quinoa. Season with salt and pepper.
4. Poach the eggs in a separate saucepan of simmering water.
5. Top the quinoa and veggie mixture with a poached egg.

Features and Variations:

➤ Customize using your favorite vegetables.
➤ For added fiber, sprinkle with chia or flax seeds.
➤ For a low-fat alternative, try using egg whites.

Utensils needed include a saucepan, skillet, and pot for poaching eggs.

Recipe #2: Avocado and Salmon Toast

Rich in omega-3 fatty acids and monounsaturated fats, this avocado and salmon toast is a tasty and heart-healthy breakfast alternative for people with a fatty liver.

Ingredient list:

- 4 pieces of whole grain bread - 2 ripe avocados (mashed)

- 200 grams smoked salmon

- One lemon, juiced

- Add salt and pepper to taste. - Garnish with fresh dill.

4 servings.

Procedure:

1. Toast whole-grain bread pieces.

2. Spread the mashed avocado evenly across each slice.

3. Spread smoked salmon over the avocado.

4. Drizzle lemon juice on top and season with salt and pepper.

5. Garnish with fresh dill.

Features and Variations:

- Replace whole-grain bread with gluten-free options.

- Top with a poached or cooked egg for added protein.

Utensils required: Toaster or toaster oven.

Recipe #3: Berry and Almond Smoothie Bowl

This smoothie bowl contains antioxidants and good fats, making it a nutritious and refreshing breakfast alternative for those with fatty livers.

Ingredients:

- 2 cups mixed berries (strawberries, blueberries, raspberries)
- 1 sliced banana.
- 1/4 cup almond butter.
- One cup unsweetened almond milk.
- Two teaspoons of chia seeds
- 1/4 cup sliced almonds

Number of Serving: 2

Instructions:

1. Blend berries, banana, almond butter, and almond milk. Blend until smooth.
2. Pour the smoothie into bowls.
3. Finish with chia seeds and sliced almonds.

Features and Variations:

- Try other berries for diversity.

- For added fiber, add 1 tablespoon flaxseed.

Utensils needed: Blender.

Recipe #4: Spinach and Feta Omelette

This spinach and feta omelette is high in protein and contains vitamins and minerals that are essential to liver health.

Ingredient list:

- four big eggs.
- 1 cup chopped fresh spinach
- 1/4 cup crumbled feta cheese.
- One tablespoon of olive oil.
- Add salt and pepper to taste.

Number of Serving: 2

Instructions:

1. 1: In a bowl, whisk the eggs. Season with salt and pepper.
2. Heat olive oil in a nonstick pan over medium heat.
3. Add the chopped spinach to the pan and cook until wilted.
4. Pour the whisked eggs over the spinach, allowing them to set slightly.
5. Sprinkle crumbled feta on one side of the omelette and fold the other half over it.
6. Cook the eggs until they are completely set.

Variations:

- Add diced tomatoes or bell peppers for more vegetables.

- For a lower-fat variation, combine whole eggs with egg whites.

Utensils required: Nonstick skillet.

Recipe #5: Chia Seed Pudding Parfait

⟷

Enjoy a tasty and nutritious chia seed pudding parfait with omega-3 fatty acids to support a fatty liver diet.

⟷

Ingredient list:

- 1/4 cup chia seeds.

- One cup unsweetened coconut milk.

- 1 teaspoon vanilla essence

- 2 tablespoons honey or maple syrup.

- 1 cup mixed fresh berries (strawberries and blueberries)

- 1/4 cup chopped walnuts.

Serves: 2

Directions:

1. In a dish, mix chia seeds, coconut milk, vanilla essence, and sweetener. Stir thoroughly and refrigerate for at least 4 hours or overnight to allow the chia seeds to absorb the liquid.
2. Place the chia seed pudding in serving glasses and top with fresh berries.
3. Top with chopped walnuts.

Features and Variations:

- Try other plant-based milks.

- Add a spoonful of Greek yogurt for added creaminess.

Utensils needed: Mixing bowl and serving glasses.

Recipe 6: Sweet Potato and Turkey Breakfast Hash.

←——————————————————————————→

Start your day with a nutrient-rich sweet potato and turkey breakfast hash. This meal is high in lean protein and complex carbs, making it an excellent choice for a fatty liver-friendly diet.

←——————————————————————————→

Ingredients:

- 2 medium sweet potatoes, peeled and diced
- 1 pound lean mince turkey
- 1 chopped onion
- 1 chopped bell pepper.
- 2 garlic cloves, minced
- Add 1 teaspoon ground cumin
- 1 teaspoon smoked paprika.
- Salt and pepper to taste.
- Garnish with fresh cilantro.

4 servings.

Instructions:

1. Cook ground turkey in a large pan till golden. Remove the surplus fat.
2. In the pan, combine the diced sweet potatoes, onion, bell pepper, and garlic. Cook veggies until they are soft.
3. Sprinkle with ground cumin, smoked paprika, salt, and pepper.
4. Before serving, garnish with chopped fresh cilantro.

Features and Variations:

- Try replacing sweet potatoes with butternut squash for a distinct flavor.

- Finish with a dollop of Greek yogurt for extra richness.

Utensils required: Large skillet.

Recipe #7: Greek Yogurt Parfait with Berries and Granola

Enjoy a protein-rich Greek yogurt parfait with berries and granola. This breakfast alternative is not only delicious but also contains probiotics that promote digestive health.

Ingredients:

- 2 cups Greek yogurt.
- 1 cup mixed berries (strawberries, blueberries, raspberries),
- 1/2 cup granola,
- 2 tablespoons honey.
- Mint leaves as garnish.

Serves: 2

Procedure:

1. Layer Greek yogurt, mixed berries, and granola in serving glasses.

2. Drizzle the honey over each layer.

3. Repeat the layers until the glass is full.

4. Just before serving, garnish with mint leaves.

Features and Variations:

- Choose a granola with little added sugars.

- For added fiber, sprinkle with chia seeds.

Utensils needed: Serving glasses.

Recipe 8: Eggs and Vegetable Breakfast Muffins

Try these egg and veggie breakfast muffins for a quick and nutritious meal. They're a fantastic choice for a fatty liver diet, as they're high in protein and vegetables.

Ingredient list:

For this recipe, you'll need 6 big eggs, 1 cup sliced bell peppers, 1 cup chopped spinach, 1/2 cup crumbled feta cheese, salt and pepper to taste, and cooking spray.

Servings: 6 muffins.

Procedures:

1: Preheat oven to 350°F (175°C) and oil muffin pan with cooking spray.

2. In a bowl, mix together the eggs and season with salt and pepper.

3. Add sliced bell peppers, chopped spinach, and crumbled feta.

4. Pour the egg mixture into the muffin cups, filling them about 3/4 full.

5. Bake the muffins for 20-25 minutes, or until they're firm and gently brown.

Features and Variations:

- Customize using your favorite vegetables.

- For more taste, add a dab of spicy sauce.

Utensils needed: Muffin tin

Recipe 9: Overnight Oats with Almond Butter and Banana

⬌

Simplify your mornings with these nutritious overnight oats with almond butter and banana. This make-ahead breakfast is high in fiber, healthy fats, and potassium.

⬌

Ingredient list:

- 1 cup rolled oats,
- 1 cup unsweetened almond milk,
- 2 tablespoons almond butter,
- One sliced banana.
- One spoonful of chia seeds
- One spoonful of honey.

Serves: 2

Instructions:

1. In a jar or container, add rolled oats, almond milk, almond butter, sliced banana, chia seeds, and honey.
2. Stir carefully to ensure the oats are completely submerged.
3. Store in the refrigerator overnight.
4. Re-stir before serving.

Features and Variations:

- Use natural almond butter with no extra sugar.

- Add a sprinkling of chopped nuts for extra crunch.

Utensils required: Jar or container.

Recipe 10: Green Smoothie With Kale and Pineapple

Energize your morning with a delicious green smoothie with kale and pineapple. This smoothie, which is high in vitamins and antioxidants, is a pleasant approach to support a fatty liver diet.

Ingredients:

- 2 cups kale with stems removed.

- One cup of pineapple pieces

- One banana.

- 1/2 cucumber, cut.

- One cup coconut water.

- Ice cubes (Optional)

Serves: 2

Instructions:

1. Blend kale, pineapple, banana, cucumber, and coconut water.

2. Blend until smooth.

3. If desired, add more ice cubes and combine again.

4. Pour into glasses and serve immediately.

Features and Variations:

- Add a handful of mint leaves for freshness.

- Add a scoop of protein powder to improve the protein content.

Utensils needed: Blender.

Recipe 11: Buckwheat pancakes with mixed berry compote

Indulge in nutritious buckwheat pancakes topped with a tasty mixed berry compote. Buckwheat, a gluten-free grain, contributes fiber and minerals to this delicious meal.

Ingredient List for Buckwheat Pancakes:

- Use 1 cup of buckwheat flour and 1 teaspoon of baking powder.
- 1/2 teaspoon cinnamon
- One cup almond milk.
- One huge egg.
- Two tablespoons maple syrup.
- Cooking Spray for the Pan

For mixed berry compote:

1 cup mixed berries (strawberries, blueberries, raspberries) with 2 tablespoons honey and 1 teaspoon lemon juice.

Procedure for Buckwheat Pancakes:

1. In a mixing bowl, combine buckwheat flour, baking powder, cinnamon, almond milk, egg, and maple syrup; whisk until smooth.
2. Preheat a griddle or nonstick pan and gently cover with cooking spray.
3. Pour 1/4 cup batter on the griddle for each pancake.
4. Cook until bubbles appear on the surface, then turn and continue cooking until both sides are golden brown.

For mixed berry compote:

1. In a saucepan, blend the berries, honey, and lemon juice.
2. Cook over medium heat until the berries are broken down and the sauce thickens slightly.

Features and Variations: - Try other berry combinations.

- Top with a spoonful of Greek yogurt for extra richness.

Utensils required: griddle or nonstick pan, saucepan.

Recipe 12: Turmeric and Ginger Smoothie Bowl

Start your day with a turmeric and ginger smoothie bowl, which is both colorful and anti-inflammatory. This bowl, which is high in antioxidants and immune-boosting nutrients, is a delicious approach to promote liver health.

Ingredients:

- One frozen banana.
- One cup of frozen mango chunks
- 1/2 teaspoon powdered turmeric,
- 1 teaspoon grated ginger.
- One cup coconut water.
- Toppings include sliced kiwi, shredded coconut, and chia seeds.

Serves: 2

Instructions:

1. Blend frozen banana, mango, turmeric, ginger, and coconut water.
2. Blend until smooth.
3. Pour into bowls and garnish with sliced kiwi, shredded coconut, and chia seeds.

Features and Variations:

- Adjust thickness by adding more or less coconut water.

- Add a handful of spinach for an added nutritious boost.

Utensils needed: Blender.

Recipe 13: Whole Wheat Blueberry Muffins.

Headnote: Enjoy guilt-free whole wheat blueberry muffins with minimal sugar and high fiber. These muffins provide a delightful and nutritious morning alternative.

Ingredient list:

- 1 1/2 cups whole wheat flour,
- 1/2 cup oats,
- 1/2 cup coconut sugar,
- 1 teaspoon baking powder.
- One-half teaspoon baking soda
- 1/4 teaspoon salt,
- 1 cup Greek yogurt.
- 1/4 cup melted coconut oil
- 2 big eggs.
- 1 tsp vanilla essence,
- 1 cup fresh or frozen blueberries.

Servings: 12 muffins.

Instructions:

1. 1: Preheat oven to 350°F (175°C) and line muffin tray with paper liners.
2. In a bowl, combine whole wheat flour, oats, coconut sugar, baking powder, baking soda, and salt.
3. In another dish, combine the Greek yogurt, melted coconut oil, eggs, and vanilla essence.
4. Mix wet and dry ingredients until just combined, then stir in blueberries.
5. Pour the mixture equally into the muffin cups and bake for 18-20 minutes, or until a toothpick comes out clean.

Features and Variations: - Add maple syrup as a natural sweetener.

- Sprinkle oats on top for texture.

Utensils needed: Muffin tin and paper liners.

Recipe 14: Vegetable and Goat Cheese Frittata

This vegetable and goat cheese frittata is a protein-rich and tasty choice for a fatty liver diet. It's an excellent breakfast option, packed with vibrant veggies and creamy goat cheese.

Ingredients:

- 6 big eggs.
- 1/2 cup halved cherry tomatoes,
- 1/2 cup diced bell peppers,
- 1/2 cup sliced zucchini,
- 1/4 cup finely chopped red onion,
- 1/4 cup crumbled goat cheese.
- One tablespoon of olive oil.
- Salt and pepper to taste.
- Garnish with fresh basil.

4 servings.

Instructions:

1. 1: Preheat the oven to 375°F (190°C).
2. In an oven-safe skillet, heat the olive oil over medium heat.
3. Combine the cherry tomatoes, bell peppers, zucchini, and red onion. Sauté the veggies until they are slightly soft.
4. In a bowl, combine the eggs, salt, and pepper. Pour the mixture over the veggies.
5. Sprinkle the crumbled goat cheese over top.
6. Place the pan in the preheated oven and bake for 15-18 minutes, or until the frittata is set.
7. Finish with fresh basil before serving.

Features and Variations: - Add spinach or kale for more greens.

- Replace goat cheese with feta for a distinct taste.

Utensils required: oven-safe skillet.

Recipe 15: Almond and Banana Protein Smoothie.

Fuel your day with a protein-rich almond and banana smoothie. This smoothie, made with almonds, bananas, and protein powder, is a delicious and nutritious morning option.

Ingredient list:

- 1 cup unsweetened almond milk
- 1 banana.
- 2 tablespoons almond butter
- 1 scoop vanilla protein powder.
- One spoonful of chia seeds
- Ice cubes (Optional)

Serves: 2

Instructions:

1. 1: In a blender, mix almond milk, banana, almond butter, protein powder, and chia seeds.
2. Blend until smooth.
3. If desired, add more ice cubes and combine again.
4. Pour into glasses and enjoy.

Features and Variations:

- Use high-quality protein powder with minimum additives.

- Add a spoonful of honey for extra sweetness.

Utensils needed: blender.

Recipe 16: Spinach and Mushroom Breakfast Burrito.

This Spinach and Mushroom Breakfast Burrito is a delicious way to start the day. It's a tasty alternative for individuals on a fatty liver diet, thanks to its leafy greens and savory mushrooms.

Ingredient list:

- Four whole grain or spinach tortillas.
- 1 cup chopped baby spinach
- 1 cup sliced mushrooms.
- Four eggs, beaten
- 1/2 cup black beans (drained and rinsed)
- 1/4 cup crumbled feta cheese.
- Salsa and avocado slices to serve.
- Add salt and pepper to taste.

4 servings.

Instructions:

1. Sauté mushrooms in a pan until golden brown. Add the chopped spinach and simmer until wilted.
2. Push the vegetables to one side of the pan, then pour beaten eggs into the vacant space and scramble until thoroughly done.
3. Combine the eggs, spinach, and mushrooms, then toss in the black beans.
4. Warm the tortillas and ladle the egg and veggie mixture onto them.
5. Top with feta crumbles, salsa, and avocado slices. Season with salt and pepper.

Features and Variations:

- Add a dash of spicy sauce for more flavor.

- Use whole eggs or egg whites, whatever you choose.

Utensils needed: Skillet.

Recipe 17: Cinnamon Apple Quinoa Porridge.

←───→

Enjoy a liver-friendly Cinnamon Apple Quinoa Porridge. Quinoa offers nutrition, while cinnamon-spiced apples give sweetness without adding sugar.

←───→

Ingredients:

- 1 cup washed quinoa.
- 2 cups almond milk,
- 2 apples (peeled, cored, and chopped),
- 1 teaspoon ground cinnamon.
- One tablespoon maple syrup (optional)
- Chopped nuts as garnish

4 servings.

Instructions:

1. In a saucepan, mix quinoa and almond milk. Bring to a boil, then decrease heat, cover, and simmer for 15-20 minutes, or until the quinoa is done.
2. In a separate skillet, sauté the diced apples and cinnamon until soft.
3. Add the cinnamon-spiced apples to the cooked quinoa.
4. If preferred, drizzle with maple syrup and serve with chopped nuts.

Features and Variations:

- Choose your preferred plant-based milk.

- Finish with a dollop of Greek yogurt for extra richness.

Utensils needed: Saucepan

Recipe 18: Smashed Avocado and Tomato Toast.

Smashed Avocado and Tomato Toast is a simple yet delicious way to elevate your morning. It's a quick and delicious solution for individuals with a fatty liver, thanks to its high content of beneficial fats and antioxidants.

Ingredient list:

- 4 pieces of whole grain bread

- 2 ripe avocados (mashed)

- 2 sliced tomatoes and fresh basil leaves.

- Drizzle with olive oil.

- Season with salt and pepper.

4 servings.

Procedure:

1. Toast whole-grain bread pieces.

2. Spread the mashed avocado evenly across each slice.

3. Arrange tomato slices on top of the avocado.

4. Garnish with fresh basil leaves.

5. Drizzle with olive oil, then season with salt and pepper.

Features and Variations:

- Add red pepper flakes for a bit of spiciness.

- Use multigrain or seeded bread to add texture.

Utensils Required: Toaster or toaster oven.

Recipe 19: Pomegranate and Walnut Overnight Oatmeal

Enjoy the sweet and tangy tastes of Pomegranate and Walnut Overnight Oats. This make-ahead breakfast is rich in antioxidants and omega-3 fatty acids, making it both healthful and tasty.

Ingredients:

- 1 cup rolled oats, 1 cup unsweetened almond milk.
- 1/2 cup pomegranate arils.
- 1/4 cup chopped walnuts.
- One spoonful of maple syrup.
- 1/2 teaspoon of vanilla essence.

Serves: 2

Instructions:

1. Combine rolled oats, almond milk, pomegranate arils, chopped walnuts, maple syrup, and vanilla essence in a jar or container.
2. Stir carefully to ensure the oats are completely submerged.
3. Store in the refrigerator overnight.
4. Re-stir before serving.

Features and Variations:

- Consider using almonds or pecans instead.

- Drizzle with honey before serving.

Utensils required: Jar or container.

Recipe #20: Salmon and Dill Egg Muffins

These Salmon and Dill Egg Muffins provide a protein-rich and tasty breakfast. They're the ideal savory alternative, with omega-3 fatty acids from salmon and fresh dill for extra brightness.

Ingredients:

- 6 big eggs.
- 1/2 cup flaked cooked salmon
- 2 teaspoons chopped fresh dill.
- Finely chop 1/4 cup red onion
- Season with salt and pepper to taste
- Use cooking spray.

Servings: 6 muffins.

Procedure:

1. Heat the oven to 350°F (175°C) and oil a muffin tray with cooking spray.
2. In a bowl, combine the eggs, flakes salmon, fresh dill, red onion, salt, and pepper.
3. Pour the egg mixture into the muffin cups, filling them about 3/4 full.
4. Bake for 15–18 minutes, or until the muffins are firm and gently brown.

Features and Variations:

- Add cream cheese for more richness.

- For a flavor explosion, sprinkle with capers.

Utensils needed: Muffin tin

Chapter 3: Lunch
1. Grilled Lemon-Herb Salmon Salad

This salad has grilled salmon and a tangy lemon herb dressing. This recipe is packed with omega-3 fatty acids, making it ideal for a light and healthy lunch.

Ingredient list:

- 4 salmon fillets
- 1 tablespoon olive oil.
- Salt and pepper to taste.
- 6 cups of mixed salad greens.
- 1 cup halved cherry tomatoes
- 1 sliced cucumber.
- 1/4 cup fresh parsley, chopped

Number of servings: four

Instructions:

1. Preheat the grill to medium-high heat.
2. Drizzle olive oil over salmon fillets and season with salt and pepper.
3. Grill the salmon for 4-5 minutes on each side, or until cooked through.
4. In a large mixing bowl, combine salad greens, cherry tomatoes, cucumber, and parsley.
5. Place the cooked salmon on top of the salad.
6. Drizzle with lemon herb dressing (see Notes for recipe).
7. Serve right away and enjoy this heart-healthy, fatty liver-friendly dinner.

Features and Variations:

- Lemon Herb Dressing: Whisk together 2 tablespoons olive oil, 2 tablespoons lemon juice, 1 teaspoon Dijon mustard, 1 clove chopped garlic, salt, and pepper.
- Variation: Replace the salmon with grilled chicken for an alternative protein choice.

Utensils Required: Grill and tongs.

2. Quinoa and Roasted Vegetable Stuffed Bell Pepper

This vibrant bell pepper dish with quinoa and roasted veggies is a healthful lunch choice for persons with fatty livers.

Ingredients:

- 4 halved bell peppers with seeds removed
- 1 cup cooked quinoa.
- 2 cups roasted veggies (zucchini, bell peppers, cherry tomatoes)
- 1 cup drained and washed black beans.
- 1 teaspoon cumin,
- Salt and pepper to taste,
- 1/4 cup chopped fresh cilantro.

Number of servings: four

Instructions:

1. Preheat the oven to 375°F (190°C).
2. In a bowl, mix the cooked quinoa, roasted veggies, black beans, cumin, salt, and pepper.
3. Fill each bell pepper half with quinoa mixture.
4. Arrange the filled peppers in a baking tray and cover with foil.
5. Bake for 25–30 minutes, or until the peppers are soft.
6. Before serving, garnish with chopped fresh cilantro.

Features and Variations:

Variation: For added protein, stir in lean ground turkey or chicken with the quinoa.

Utensils Required: Baking dish and foil.

3. Chickpea and Spinach Stir-Fry

This quick and easy stir-fry with chickpeas and spinach is a tasty and liver-friendly dinner. Ideal for a fuss-free lunch.

Ingredient list:

- 2 tablespoons olive oil,
- 1 thinly sliced onion,
- 2 minced garlic cloves.
- One can (15 oz) of drained and washed chickpeas
- 4 cups fresh spinach leaves,
- 1 teaspoon ground cumin,
- Salt and pepper to taste,
- Lemon wedges for serving.

Number of servings: four

Instructions:

1. Heat olive oil in a large pan over medium heat.
2. Add the chopped onion and minced garlic and cook until softened.
3. Stir in the chickpeas and simmer for 3-4 minutes.
4. Add the spinach, cumin, salt, and pepper and simmer until the spinach wilts.
5. Before serving, squeeze some fresh lemon juice over the stir-fry.

Features and Variations:

Variation: Add cherry tomatoes or bell peppers for color and flavor.

Utensils: Skillet.

4. Turkey and Vegetable Lettuce Wrap

These lettuce wraps with lean ground turkey and veggies are ideal for a low-fat, liver-friendly lunch.

Ingredient list:

- 1 pound lean ground turkey,
- 1 tablespoon olive oil,
- 1 chopped onion.
- Two julienned carrots and one chopped zucchini.
- 3 garlic cloves, minced
- One tablespoon of low-sodium soy sauce
- 1 teaspoon powdered ginger
- 1 head of iceberg lettuce, leaves separated

Number of servings: four

Instructions:

1. Brown ground turkey in olive oil in a large pan over medium heat.
2. Add the chopped onion, julienned carrots, diced zucchini, and minced garlic; sauté until soft.
3. Stir in the soy sauce and ground ginger, and simmer for another 2 minutes.
4. Spoon the turkey and vegetable mixture into lettuce leaves to form wraps.

Features and Variations:

Variation: Use lean ground chicken or tofu instead of turkey to change the protein source.

Utensils Required: Skillet.

5. Baked Sweet Potato and Lentil Patties.

These baked sweet potato and lentil patties are not only tasty, but also high in fiber and minerals. A delicious choice for those looking for a plant-based, liver-friendly lunch.

Ingredient list:

- 2 medium sweet potatoes.

- 1 cup lentils.

- 1/2 cup bread crumbs.

- 1 teaspoon cumin

- 1 teaspoon paprika.

- Salt and pepper to taste.

- 2 tablespoons olive oil.

Number of servings: four

Instructions:

1. Preheat the oven to 375°F (190°C) and prepare a baking sheet with parchment paper.
2. In a bowl, mix the mashed sweet potatoes, cooked lentils, breadcrumbs, cumin, paprika, salt, and pepper.
3. Shape the mixture into patties and arrange on the prepared baking sheet.
4. Brush the patties with olive oil and bake for 25–30 minutes, turning halfway through.

Features and Variations:

- Add finely chopped spinach or kale to the patty mixture for additional greens.

Utensils Required: Baking sheet and parchment paper.

6. Lemon Garlic Shrimp and Asparagus Stir-Fry.

This stir-fry combines luscious shrimp and crisp asparagus with a light lemon garlic sauce. A simple and delectable lunch alternative for people who want to incorporate seafood in their fatty liver diet.

Ingredient list:

- 1 lb shrimp (peeled and deveined)
- 1 bunch asparagus (trimmed and chopped into bite-sized portions)
- 2 tablespoons olive oil
- 3 minced garlic cloves.
- Zest and juice from 1 lemon
- Salt and pepper to taste.
- Garnish with fresh parsley.

Number of servings: four

Procedure:

1. Heat olive oil in a large pan over medium-high heat.

2. Cook the shrimp for 2-3 minutes on each side, or until pink.

3. Add the minced garlic and asparagus; sauté until tender-crisp.

4. Mix in the lemon zest, juice, salt, and pepper.

5. Garnish with fresh parsley and serve immediately.

Features and Variations:

Variation: Add cherry tomatoes or bell peppers for color and flavor.

Utensils: Skillet.

7. Mediterranean Chickpea Salad.

Enjoy the vivid flavors of the Mediterranean with this hearty chickpea salad. It's a delicious and filling lunch alternative, full of fresh veggies and herbs.

Ingredients:

- Two cans (15 oz each) of drained and washed chickpeas.
- 1 diced cucumber,
- 1 cup split cherry tomatoes,
- 1/2 finely chopped red onion,
- 1/2 cup sliced Kalamata olives,
- 1/4 cup crumbled feta cheese
- Two teaspoons of olive oil.
- Juice from 1 lemon
- One teaspoon dried oregano.
- Salt and pepper to taste.

Number of servings: four

Procedure:

1. In a large bowl, mix chickpeas, cucumber, cherry tomatoes, red onion, olives, and feta cheese.
2. In a small dish, combine the olive oil, lemon juice, dried oregano, salt, and pepper.
3. Pour the dressing over the salad and gently toss to mix.
4. Serve chilled and enjoy this cool Mediterranean cuisine.

Features and Variations:

Variation: Add grilled chicken or shrimp for an additional protein boost.

Utensils Required: Mixing bowls.

8. Teriyaki Chicken and Broccoli Stir-Fry

Enjoy the delights of a traditional teriyaki stir-fry with this liver-friendly version that includes lean chicken breast and nutritious vegetables. A quick and tasty lunch choice.

Ingredients:

- 1 lb thinly sliced boneless, skinless chicken breast
- 2 tablespoons low-sodium teriyaki sauce.
- Two teaspoons of soy sauce.
- 1 tablespoon honey,
- 1 tablespoon sesame oil,
- 1 tablespoon olive oil.
- Two cups of broccoli florets
- Two green onions, sliced
- Sesame seeds as garnish

Number of servings: four

Procedures:

1. Marinate sliced chicken in teriyaki sauce for 15 minutes.

2. In a large pan, heat the olive and sesame oils over medium-high heat.

3. Add the marinated chicken and heat until browned and cooked through.

4. Add the broccoli and cook until tender-crisp.

5. Stir in the soy sauce, honey, and green onions.

6. Sprinkle with sesame seeds and serve over brown rice or quinoa.

Features and Variations:

- Substitute tofu or shrimp for chicken.

Utensils Required: Skillet.

9. Spinach and Mushroom Quiche Cups.

Enjoy a delicious brunch or lunch with these individual spinach and mushroom quiche cups. They are a pleasant and liver-friendly choice that is high in greens and flavorful mushrooms.

Ingredients:

- 6 big eggs.
- 1 cup chopped baby spinach,
- 1 cup finely diced mushrooms,
- 1/2 cup crumbled feta cheese,
- 1/4 cup milk.
- Salt and pepper to taste.
- Cooking spray.

Number of servings: six

Instructions:

1. Preheat oven to 375°F (190°C) and oil muffin pan with cooking spray.
2. In a dish, combine the eggs, milk, salt, and pepper.
3. Divide the chopped spinach, mushrooms, and feta cheese amongst the muffin cups.
4. Pour the egg mixture over the veggies and cheese.
5. Bake the quiche cups for 20-25 minutes, or until they are firm and gently brown.
6. Let cool for a few minutes before serving.

Features and Variations:

Variation: Add chopped tomatoes or bell peppers for more flavor.

Utensils Required: Muffin tin.

10. Baked cod with lemon herb crust.

For a delicious lunch, try this baked fish with a lemon herb crust. It's a nutritious option for folks with fatty liver disease because it's high in omega-3 fatty acids.

Ingredients:

- 4 fish fillets,
- 1/4 cup breadcrumbs.
- Zest from 1 lemon
- Chop 2 tablespoons of fresh parsley.
- 1 tablespoon of olive oil.
- Salt and pepper to taste.
- Lemon wedges.

Number of servings: four

Instructions:

1. Preheat the oven to 400°F (200°C) and prepare a baking sheet with parchment paper.
2. In a mixing bowl, add breadcrumbs, lemon zest, chopped parsley, olive oil, salt, and pepper.
3. Arrange the fish fillets on the prepared baking sheet.
4. Apply the breadcrumb mixture to the top of each fillet.
5. Bake for 15-20 minutes, or until the fish flaked easily with a fork.
6. Add lemon wedges for an added punch of flavor.

Features and Variations:

Variation: Replace cod with another white fish, such as halibut or tilapia.

Utensils Required: Baking sheet and parchment paper.

11. Roasted Vegetable and Quinoa Stuffed Portobello Mushrooms

Stuffed portobello mushrooms with roasted veggies and protein-rich quinoa make a delicious lunch option. A tasty and fulfilling solution for a fatty liver diet.

Ingredient list:

- 4 big portobello mushrooms (stems removed),
- 1 cup cooked quinoa,
- 1 cup chopped cherry tomatoes,
- 1 diced zucchini,
- 1 diced red bell pepper.
- 2 garlic cloves, minced
- 2 tablespoons balsamic vinegar,
- 2 tablespoons olive oil.
- Salt and pepper to taste.
- Garnish with fresh basil.

Number of servings: four

Instructions:

1. Preheat the oven to 375°F (190°C).
2. Arrange portobello mushrooms on a baking pan.
3. In a bowl, combine the cooked quinoa, cherry tomatoes, zucchini, red bell pepper, garlic, balsamic vinegar, olive oil, salt, and pepper.
4. Stuff each mushroom with quinoa mixture.
5. Bake for 20–25 minutes, or until the mushrooms are soft.
6. Before serving, garnish with fresh basil leaves.

Features and Variations:

Variation: Add crumbled feta or goat cheese for an additional layer of flavor.

Utensils Required: Baking sheet.

12. Lentil And Vegetable Soup

Warm up with lentil and vegetable soup, rich in nutrients and mild on the liver. This easy and hearty soup is ideal for a nutritious lunch.

Ingredients:

- 1 cup dry green or brown lentils, rinsed
- 1 chopped onion
- two carrots, peeled and chopped
- Two celery stalks, chopped
- 3 garlic cloves, minced
- One can (14 ounces).
- Diced tomatoes
- 6 cups vegetable broth,
- 1 teaspoon cumin,
- 1 teaspoon turmeric.
- Salt and pepper to taste.
- Garnish with fresh parsley.

Number of servings: six

Instructions:

1. In a large saucepan, add lentils, onion, carrots, celery, garlic, chopped tomatoes, vegetable broth, cumin, turmeric, salt, and pepper.
2. Bring to a boil, then decrease the heat and simmer for 25-30 minutes, or until the lentils are cooked.
3. Prior to serving, garnish with fresh parsley.

Features and Variations:

Variation: Add spinach or kale for more greens.

Utensils Required: Large pot.

13. Turkey and Veggie Lettuce Wrap Bowl.

Transform the lettuce wrap into a bowl with this turkey and vegetable combo. It's a filling and low-fat lunch choice that includes lean protein and colorful veggies.

Ingredient list:

- 1 pound lean ground turkey,
- 1 tablespoon olive oil,
- 1 chopped onion,
- 1 diced bell pepper.
- One cup of shredded cabbage
- 1 julienned carrot
- 3 minced garlic cloves.
- Two teaspoons of low-sodium soy sauce
- One teaspoon of sesame oil.
- 1 teaspoon grated ginger.
- Butter the lettuce leaves before serving.

Number of servings: four

Instructions:

1. Heat olive oil in a large pan over medium-high.
2. Brown ground turkey with chopped onion and garlic.
3. Combine the bell pepper, shredded cabbage, julienned carrot, soy sauce, sesame oil, and grated ginger.
4. Cook veggies until they are soft.
5. Serve the turkey and vegetable combination in butter lettuce leaves.

Features and Variations:

Variation: Add water chestnuts or bamboo shoots for extra crunch.

Utensils Required: Skillet.

14. Broccoli and Chicken Quinoa Bowl.

Enjoy this nutritious broccoli and chicken quinoa meal. It's a nutritious lunch option for individuals looking to improve their liver health, since it's high in fiber, protein, and vitamins.

Ingredient list:

- 1 cup cooked quinoa
- 1 lb boneless, skinless chicken breast (cooked and shredded)
- 2 cups broccoli florets, steamed
- 1 thinly sliced red bell pepper
- 1/4 cup sliced almonds.
- 2 tablespoons olive oil,
- 2 teaspoons balsamic vinegar,
- Salt and pepper to taste.

Number of servings: four

Instructions:

1. In a large bowl, mix cooked quinoa, shredded chicken, steamed broccoli, sliced red bell pepper, and almonds.
2. In a small bowl, combine olive oil, balsamic vinegar, salt, and pepper.
3. Pour the dressing over the quinoa and toss to incorporate.
4. Serve and enjoy this nutritious and tasty dish.

Features and Variations:

Variation: Add cherry tomatoes or avocado for added freshness.

Utensils Required: Mixing bowls.

15. Sweet Potato and Black Bean Salad.

Enjoy a delicious sweet potato and black bean salad. This salad, which is high in fiber and minerals, is not only tasty but also good for people who have fatty livers.

Ingredients:

-   2 roasted sweet potatoes
-   1 can (15 oz) of drained and rinsed black beans.
-   1 finely sliced red onion
-   1 diced red bell pepper.
-   1/4 cup fresh cilantro, chopped
-   Juice from two limes
-   2 tablespoons olive oil,
-   1 teaspoon cumin,
-   Salt and pepper to taste.

Number of servings: four

Procedure:

1. In a large mixing bowl, add roasted sweet potatoes, black beans, sliced red onion, diced red bell pepper, and cilantro.
2. In a small bowl, combine the lime juice, olive oil, cumin, salt, and pepper.
3. Toss the lettuce with the dressing until well coated.
4. Serve chilled and enjoy the flavors of this healthy sweet potato and black bean combo.

Features and Variations:

- Variation: Add diced avocado for extra richness.

- Utensils Required: Mixing bowls.

16. Mediterranean Grilled Chicken Skewers.

Enjoy these Mediterranean-inspired grilled chicken skewers. These skewers, marinated in herbs and spices, are a delicious and protein-rich lunch choice.

Ingredient list:

- 1.5 pounds of boneless, skinless chicken breasts chopped into bits.
- 1/4 cup olive oil,
- 2 teaspoons lemon juice,
- 2 minced garlic cloves.
- One teaspoon dried oregano.
- One teaspoon of paprika.
- Salt and pepper to taste.
- Cherry tomatoes and red onion wedges to skewer.

Number of servings: four

Instructions:

1. In a bowl, combine olive oil, lemon juice, garlic, oregano, paprika, salt, and pepper.
2. Let the chicken pieces marinate in the marinade for at least 30 minutes.
3. Thread marinated chicken, cherry tomatoes, and red onion wedges on skewers.
4. Grill the skewers over medium-high heat until the chicken is cooked through.
5. Serve with a side of full grain couscous or quinoa.

Features and Variations:

Variation: Add bell peppers or zucchini to the skewers for more veggies.

Required utensils: Grill and skewers.

17. Cabbage and Apple Slaw with Grilled Salmon

Enjoy grilled salmon with a crisp cabbage and apple salad for a delicious meal. It's a delicious and liver-friendly option with plenty of crunch and omega-3 fatty acids.

Ingredients:

- 4 salmon fillets,
- 4 cups thinly sliced green cabbage,
- 2 julienned apples,
- 1/4 cup Greek yogurt.
- 2 tablespoons apple cider vinegar,
- 1 tablespoon honey.
- Salt and pepper to taste.

Number of servings: four

Instructions:

1. Preheat the grill to medium-high heat.
2. Season salmon fillets with salt and pepper, then cook for 4-5 minutes per side.
3. In a large mixing bowl, combine the sliced cabbage and julienned apple.
4. In a small dish, combine the Greek yogurt, apple cider vinegar, honey, salt, and pepper.
5. Toss the cabbage and apple combination in the dressing.
6. Serve the cooked salmon on top of the slaw.

Features and Variations:

Variation: Use plain yogurt or a dairy-free option for the slaw dressing.

Utensils required: Grill.

18. Quinoa and Vegetable Stuffed Bell Peppers.

These stuffed bell peppers combine quinoa and a variety of veggies for a nutritious meal. This nutrient-dense meal is a bright and tasty choice for a liver-friendly lunch.

Ingredients:

- 4 halved bell peppers (seeds removed)
- 1 cup cooked quinoa
- 1 cup drained and rinsed black beans
- 1 cup corn kernels
- 1 cup diced tomatoes
- 1 teaspoon cumin
- 1 teaspoon chili powder
- Salt and pepper.
- Top with shredded cheese (optional).

Number of servings: four

Instructions:

1. Preheat the oven to 375°F (190°C).
2. In a bowl, combine the cooked quinoa, black beans, corn, chopped tomatoes, cumin, chili powder, salt, and pepper.
3. Fill each bell pepper half with quinoa mixture.
4. If desired, add shredded cheese.
5. Bake for 25–30 minutes, or until the peppers are soft.

Features and Variations:

Variation: Add ground turkey or chicken to the quinoa mixture for more protein.

Utensils Required: Baking dish.

19. Avocado and Chickpea Lettuce Wraps.

Fresh avocado and chickpea lettuce wraps. These wraps are not only delectable, but they also include healthy fats and plant-based protein, making them an excellent choice for a liver-friendly lunch.

Ingredient list:

- 1 can (15 oz) drained and rinsed chickpeas,
- 2 diced avocados,
- 1/4 cup finely chopped red onion,
- 1/4 cup chopped fresh cilantro,
- 1 lime juice.
- Salt and pepper to taste.
- Lettuce leaves to wrap

Number of servings: four

Instructions:

1. Mash chickpeas in a bowl using a fork.

2. Combine diced avocados, red onion, cilantro, lime juice, salt, and pepper.

3. Mix thoroughly to mix.

4. Spoon the mixture onto big lettuce leaves to form wraps.

5. Serve immediately and savor this light and delicious meal.

Features and Variations:

Variation: Add cherry tomatoes or cucumber for added freshness.

Utensils Required: Mixing bowl.

20. Cauliflower Fried Rice with Shrimp.

Enjoy the taste of fried rice without the guilt with this cauliflower fried rice with shrimp. It's a low-carb, high-flavor lunch choice for individuals managing their liver health.

Ingredient list:

- 1 lb peeled and deveined shrimp,
- 1 grated head cauliflower,
- 2 chopped carrots, 1 cup peas,
- 3 sliced green onions.
- 3 garlic cloves, minced
- Two teaspoons of soy sauce.
- 1 tablespoon sesame oil
- 2 beaten eggs.
- Salt and pepper to taste.

Number of servings: four

Instructions:

1. Cook shrimp in a large pan until pink. Set aside.
2. In the same pan, cook chopped carrots, peas, green onions, and minced garlic until soft.
3. Push the veggies aside and add the beaten eggs to the pan, scrambling until done.
4. Place the grated cauliflower in the pan and simmer for 5-7 minutes.
5. Stir in the cooked shrimp, soy sauce, sesame oil, salt, and pepper.
6. Serve and enjoy the flavor of this low-carb cauliflower fried rice.

Features and Variations:

Replace shrimp with chicken or tofu for an alternative protein option.

Utensils needed: Skillet.

Chapter 4: Dinner Delicacies
Recipe #1: Grilled Lemon Garlic Salmon with Quinoa

This heart-healthy meal blends the richness of salmon with the nutty taste of quinoa, making it an excellent choice for people who have fatty livers. Salmon has omega-3 fatty acids, which aid to decrease inflammation, while quinoa is high in fiber and protein.

Ingredients:

- 4 salmon fillets
- 1 cup rinsed quinoa.
- 2 cups vegetable broth,
- 1 sliced lemon,
- 4 minced garlic cloves.
- 2 tablespoons olive oil
- 1 teaspoon dried oregano.
- Salt and pepper to taste.

The number of servings is four.

Procedure:

1. Preheat the grill to medium-high.
2. Season the salmon fillets with salt, pepper, and oregano. Drizzle with olive oil and massage each fillet with chopped garlic.
3. Arrange lemon slices on top of the salmon fillets.
4. Grill the salmon for 4-5 minutes on each side, or until it flakes easily with a fork.
5. In a saucepan, heat the vegetable broth until it boils. Add the quinoa, decrease the heat, cover, and cook for 15 minutes, or until done.
6. Place grilled salmon on a bed of prepared quinoa. Garnish with more lemon slices.

Features and Variations:

➢ For more taste, replace veggie broth with chicken broth.
➢ For a distinctive touch, try using herbs such as thyme or rosemary.
➢ For added nutrition, add cooked veggies such as asparagus or broccoli.

Utensils needed: Grill, saucepan, tongs, cutting board, knife, and serving platter.

Recipe #2: Baked Sweet Potato and Turkey Chili

This cozy and nourishing chili is low in fat and high in fiber, making it ideal for individuals on a fatty liver diet. Sweet potatoes give natural sweetness and an extra dose of vitamins.

Ingredients List

- 1 pound ground turkey,
- 2 diced sweet potatoes,
- 1 can (15 oz) drained and rinsed black beans.
- 1 can (15 oz) chopped tomatoes
- 1 diced onion.
- 2 garlic cloves, minced
- 1 tablespoon of chili powder.
- 1 teaspoon cumin,
- Salt and pepper to taste.
- 2 cups of chicken broth.

Number of servings: 6

Procedure:

1. Preheat your oven to 375°F (190°C).
2. Cook the ground turkey in a large oven-safe saucepan over medium heat. Drain any extra fat.
3. Add the onions and garlic and sauté until tender.
4. Mix in the sweet potatoes, black beans, chopped tomatoes, chili powder, cumin, salt, and pepper.
5. Pour in the chicken broth, reduce to a simmer, and cover the saucepan.
6. Place the pot in the preheated oven and bake for 30-35 minutes, or until sweet potatoes are cooked.

Features and Variations:

➢ For an extra creamy topping, use Greek yogurt or low-fat sour cream.
➢ Experiment with different beans, such as kidney beans and pinto beans.
➢ For a spicy kick, add chopped jalapeño pepper.

Utensils needed: large oven-safe saucepan, wooden spoon, cutting board, knife, can opener, and measuring spoons.

Recipe #3: Lemon Herb Grilled Chicken Salad

This light and refreshing grilled chicken salad is packed with flavor. The lean protein from chicken, paired with the sharpness of fresh veggies, making it a healthy alternative for persons with fatty liver issues.

Ingredients List:

- Two boneless, skinless chicken breasts.
- Six cups mixed salad greens.
- 1/2 cup cherry tomatoes,
- 1 cucumber (sliced)
- 1/4 cup feta cheese.
- 1/4 cup pitted Kalamata olives,
- 2 tablespoons olive oil,
- 2 tablespoons fresh lemon juice.
- One teaspoon dried oregano.
- Salt and pepper to taste.

Number of servings: 2

Procedure:

1. Preheat the grill to medium.
2. Season the chicken breasts with salt, pepper, and oregano.
3. Grill the chicken for 6-8 minutes per side, or until well done.
4. In a large mixing bowl, combine salad greens, cherry tomatoes, cucumber, feta cheese, and olives.
5. Slice the grilled chicken and place on top of the salad.
6. In a small dish, combine olive oil and lemon juice. Drizzle over salad.

Features and Variations:

➢ For an extra creamy texture, add avocado slices.
➢ Try balsamic vinaigrette as an alternate dressing.
➢ For extra flavor, grill the chicken with fresh herbs such as rosemary or thyme.

Utensils needed:

➢ Grill, tongs, large salad bowl, and whisk.
➢ Cutting board and knife.

Recipe #4: Quinoa-Stuffed Bell Peppers

These vibrant bell peppers are stuffed with a healthy quinoa filling, making them an ideal dinner for people concerned about their fatty liver. This meal is both tasty and nutritious, thanks to its high fiber and vitamin content.

Ingredients List

- 4 bell peppers cut in half and remove seeds.
- 1 cup of quinoa.
- 1 can (15 oz) of black beans drained and rinse
- 1 cup corn kernels,
- 1 cup diced tomatoes,
- 1 cup low-fat shredded cheese,
- 1 teaspoon ground cumin,
- 1 teaspoon chili powder.
- Salt and pepper to taste.
- Garnish with fresh cilantro.

The number of servings is four.

Procedure:

1. Preheat your oven to 375°F (190°C).
2. In a large mixing bowl, add the cooked quinoa, black beans, corn, chopped tomatoes, cheese, cumin, chili powder, salt, and pepper.
3. Fill the bell pepper halves with the quinoa mixture.
4. Place the filled peppers on a baking tray, cover with foil, and bake for 25–30 minutes.
5. Remove the foil and bake for 10 more minutes, or until the peppers are soft.
6. Before serving, garnish with chopped fresh cilantro.

Features and Variations:

➢ Season the filling with sautéed veggies such as zucchini or spinach.
➢ For a different texture, substitute brown rice instead of quinoa.
➢ Drizzle with salsa or Greek yogurt for extra flavor.

Utensils needed: Required items are a baking dish, mixing bowl, spoon, cutting board, knife, and foil.

Recipe #5: Mediterranean Baked Cod with Roasted Vegetables

This Mediterranean-inspired recipe combines flaky fish with a variety of colorful roasted veggies. It's a delicious and health-conscious addition to a fatty liver diet, thanks to its high omega-3 fatty acid and antioxidant content.

Ingredients List

- 4 cod fillets,
- 1 sliced zucchini,
- 1 sliced red bell pepper,
- 1 yellow bell pepper.
- One red onion, sliced
- 1 cup cherry tomatoes,
- 3 tablespoons olive oil,
- 2 tablespoons fresh lemon juice,
- 2 teaspoons dry oregano.
- Salt and pepper to taste.
- Garnish with fresh parsley.

The number of servings is four.

Procedure:

1. Preheat your oven to 400°F (200°C).
2. Arrange the cod fillets in a baking dish, surrounded by zucchini, bell peppers, red onion, and cherry tomatoes.
3. In a small bowl, combine the olive oil, lemon juice, oregano, salt, and pepper. Drizzle over the fish and veggies.
4. Bake for 20-25 minutes, or until the cod flaked easily with a fork and the veggies were soft.
5. Sprinkle with fresh parsley before serving.

Features and Variations:

- ➤ For a Mediterranean flavor, garnish with chopped olives.
- ➤ To finish the dish, serve over couscous or quinoa.
- ➤ Experiment with other white fish kinds, such as haddock and halibut.

Utensils needed: Baking dish, small basin, whisk, - Cutting Board and A knife

Recipe #6: Lentil and Vegetable Soup

This substantial, fiber-rich lentil soup is an excellent complement to a fatty liver diet. It's both filling and healthful, thanks to its vegetable and plant-based protein content.

Ingredients List:

- 1 cup dry green or brown lentils, washed
- 1 finely chopped onion,
- 2 diced carrots,
- 2 diced celery stalks.
- 3 garlic cloves, minced
- One can (14 ounces) of chopped tomatoes
- 6 cups vegetable broth,
- 1 teaspoon ground cumin,
- 1 teaspoon smoky paprika.
- 1 bay leaf,
- Salt and pepper to taste,
- Fresh parsley for garnish.

Number of servings: 6

Procedure:

1. In a large saucepan, sauté the onions, carrots, and celery until tender.
2. Combine the minced garlic, cumin, and smoked paprika. Cook for an extra minute.
3. Combine the lentils, diced tomatoes, vegetable broth, and bay leaf. Bring to a boil.
4. Reduce the heat, cover, and simmer for 25-30 minutes, or until the lentils are cooked.
5. Season with salt and pepper. Remove the bay leaf before serving.
6. Garnish with fresh parsley.

Features and Variations:

➢ For an extra serving of greens, add spinach or kale.
➢ Blend a part of the soup to achieve a creamier texture.
➢ For a brighter flavor, serve with a squeeze of lemon.

Utensils needed: large saucepan, wooden spoon, cutting board, and knife.

Recipe 7: Turkey and Vegetable Stir-Fry

This simple and colorful turkey stir-fry is a low-fat choice for a great meal. It's an easy and delectable option for folks dealing with fatty liver issues, thanks to its lean protein and colorful veggies.

Ingredients List:

- 1 pound ground turkey,
- 2 cups broccoli florets,
- 1 sliced red bell pepper,
- 1 sliced yellow bell pepper.
- 1 julienned carrot
- 3 tablespoons low-sodium soy sauce.
- One tablespoon of sesame oil.
- 2 teaspoons of minced ginger.
- 2 garlic cloves, minced
- 1 tablespoon cornstarch
- 2 tablespoons of water.
- Green onions as garnish.

The number of servings is four.

Procedure:

1. In a small bowl, combine the soy sauce, sesame oil, ginger, and garlic. Set aside.
2. In a large pan, cook the ground turkey over medium-high heat.
3. Combine broccoli, bell peppers, and carrots. Stir-fry the veggies for 5-7 minutes, or until soft and crisp.
4. Pour the soy sauce mixture over the turkey and veggies.
5. In a separate dish, combine the cornstarch and water. Add to the skillet and stir until the sauce thickens.
6. Before serving, garnish with thinly sliced green onion.

Features and Variations:

➢ Replace ground turkey with leaner ground chicken or tofu.
➢ Add snap peas or water chestnuts for extra crunch.
➢ Serve over brown or cauliflower rice.

Utensils needed: large skillet, knife, wooden spoon, small bowl, and cutting board.

Recipe 8: Spinach and Feta Stuffed Chicken Breast.

This exquisite recipe consists of chicken breasts filled with spinach and feta, providing a tasty and protein-packed choice for individuals with fatty liver issues. It's a fantastic way to get more lean protein and leafy greens into your diet.

Ingredients List:

- Four boneless and skinless chicken breasts
- 2 cups of fresh spinach,
- 1/2 cup of feta cheese,
- 2 cloves of garlic.
- 1 tablespoon olive oil
- 1 teaspoon dried oregano.
- Salt and pepper to taste.
- Toothpicks to secure.

The number of servings is four.

Procedure:

1. Preheat your oven to 375°F (190°C).
2. In a pan, cook the chopped spinach and minced garlic in olive oil until wilted.
3. Remove from heat and mix in the feta cheese, oregano, salt, and pepper.
4. Cut a pocket horizontally from each chicken breast. Stuff with the spinach-feta mixture.
5. Use toothpicks to secure the pockets, then set the chicken in a baking dish.
6. Bake the chicken for 25-30 minutes, or until well done.

Features and Variations:

➢ Use goat cheese or ricotta instead of feta.
➢ Drizzle with lemon juice before serving.
➢ Serve alongside steamed veggies or a simple salad.

Utensils needed: - Skillet, baking dish, toothpicks, and cutting board.

- A knife

Recipe 9: Quinoa and Black Bean Stuffed Peppers.

These quinoa and black bean stuffed peppers provide a filling and protein-packed meal. They are high in fiber and minerals and make an excellent addition to a fatty liver diet.

Ingredients List:

- 4 big bell peppers, halved and seeds removed
- 1 cup cooked quinoa
- 1 can (15 oz) drained and washed black beans.
- 1 cup corn kernels,
- 1 cup diced tomatoes,
- 1 cup low-fat shredded cheese,
- 1 teaspoon ground cumin,
- 1 teaspoon chili powder.
- Salt and pepper to taste.
- Garnish with fresh cilantro.

The number of servings is four.

Procedure:

1. Preheat your oven to 375°F (190°C).
2. In a large bowl, combine the cooked quinoa, black beans, corn, chopped tomatoes, cheese, cumin, chili powder, salt, and pepper.
3. Fill the bell pepper halves with the quinoa mixture.
4. Place the filled peppers on a baking tray, cover with foil, and bake for 25–30 minutes.
5. Remove the foil and bake for 10 more minutes, or until the peppers are soft.
6. Before serving, garnish with chopped fresh cilantro.

Features and Variations:

➢ Season the filling with sautéed veggies such as zucchini or spinach.
➢ For a different texture, substitute brown rice instead of quinoa.
➢ Drizzle with salsa or Greek yogurt for extra flavor.

Utensils needed: baking dish, mixing bowl, spoon, cutting board, knife, and foil.

Recipe 10: Shrimp and Vegetable Skewers with Quinoa.

These vibrant and savory shrimp and veggie skewers with quinoa make for a light and protein-packed entrée. It's an excellent choice for people trying to boost liver health, as it's high in antioxidants and omega-3 fatty acids.

Ingredients List

- 1 lb peeled and deveined shrimp
- 2 chunked bell peppers (assorted colors).
- 1 zucchini
- 1 red onion
- Two teaspoons of olive oil.
- One teaspoon of smoked paprika.
- One teaspoon dried thyme
- Salt and pepper to taste.
- 1 cup of quinoa.

The number of servings is four.

Procedure:

1. Preheat the grill to medium-high.
2. In a mixing dish, combine shrimp, bell peppers, zucchini, and red onion with olive oil, smoked paprika, thyme, salt, and pepper.
3. Thread the marinated shrimp and veggies on the moistened wooden skewers.
4. Grill the skewers for 3-4 minutes each side, or until the shrimp turn opaque and the veggies browned.
5. Serve on a bed of cooked quinoa.

Features and Variations:

➢ For added flavor, brush the skewers with a lemon-garlic marinade.
➢ Place cherry tomatoes or mushrooms on the skewers.
➢ Sprinkle with fresh parsley before serving.

Utensils needed:

To prepare, you'll need a grill, bowl, wooden skewers, tongs, cooking brush, cutting board, and knife.

Recipe 11: Baked Chicken and Vegetable Casserole.

This healthy casserole is a terrific one-dish dinner for individuals battling fatty liver issues. Packed with lean protein from chicken and a variety of bright veggies, it's a soothing and healthful alternative.

Ingredients List:

- Four boneless and skinless chicken breasts
- 2 cups sweet potatoes, peeled and diced
- 1 cup broccoli florets
- 1 cup cherry tomatoes, halved
- One red onion, sliced
- 2 tablespoons olive oil
- 2 teaspoons dried Italian herbs
- Salt and pepper to taste
- 1/2 cup low-sodium chicken broth

The number of servings is four.

Procedure:

1. Preheat your oven to 375°F (190°C).
2. Place chicken breasts in a baking dish. Surround with sweet potatoes, broccoli, cherry tomatoes, and red onion.
3. Drizzle olive oil over the ingredients, sprinkle with dried Italian herbs, salt, and pepper.
4. Pour chicken broth into the dish.
5. Bake for 30-35 minutes, or until chicken is well cooked and veggies are soft.

Features and Variations:

➤ Experiment with various veggies, such as bell peppers and asparagus.
➤ Add a sprinkle of grated Parmesan cheese before serving.
➤ Serve over quinoa or brown rice.

Utensils needed:

- Baking dish - Cutting board - Knife - Tongs

Recipe 12: Eggplant and Chickpea Curry

This vegetarian curry is a tasty and plant-based choice for people aiming to promote liver function. This recipe is both filling and healthful, thanks to the high fiber and antioxidant content of the eggplant and chickpeas.

Ingredients List

- One big eggplant
- One can (15 oz) of chickpeas drained and rinsed
- Finely slice one onion
- Two cloves garlic
- One can (14 ounces) of chopped tomatoes
- One can (14 ounces) coconut milk
- Two teaspoons curry powder.
- 1 teaspoon cumin
- 1 teaspoon ground coriander
- Salt and pepper to taste.
- Garnish with fresh cilantro.

The number of servings is four.

Procedure:

1. In a large saucepan, sauté the onions and garlic until tender.
2. Cook the chopped eggplant until it begins to brown.
3. Mix in the chickpeas, chopped tomatoes, coconut milk, curry powder, cumin, coriander, salt, and pepper.
4. Simmer for 20 to 25 minutes, or until the eggplant is soft.
5. Sprinkle with fresh cilantro and serve over cooked brown rice.

Features and Variations:

➢ To adjust the spice level, use more or less curry powder.
➢ Add spinach or kale for extra greens.
➢ For a lighter version, use low-fat yogurt instead of coconut milk.

Utensils needed:

Large saucepan, wooden spoon, cutting board, and knife.

Recipe 13: Turkey and Quinoa Stuffed Acorn Squash.

These roasted acorn squash halves packed with a flavorful blend of turkey and quinoa make a delicious and healthy addition to a fatty liver diet. The mix of lean protein and nutritious carbohydrates makes this dish both filling and tasty.

Ingredients List

- 2 halves acorn squash with seeds removed,
- 1 cup ground turkey,
- 1 cup cooked quinoa,
- 1/2 cup dried cranberries.
- 1/4 cup chopped pecans.
- 1 teaspoon ground sage,
- 1 teaspoon maple syrup.
- Salt and pepper to taste.
- Olive oil.

The number of servings is four.

Procedure:

1. Preheat your oven to 400°F (200°C).
2. Arrange acorn squash halves on a baking sheet. Drizzle olive oil and season with salt and pepper.
3. Cook ground turkey in a pan until browned. Combine cooked quinoa, cranberries, chopped pecans, sage, maple syrup, salt, and pepper. Mix thoroughly.
4. Fill each acorn squash half with the turkey-quinoa mixture.
5. Bake for 25–30 minutes, or until the squash is soft.

Features and Variations:

- Replace ground turkey with leaner ground chicken or beef.
- For a distinct nutty flavor, try walnuts instead of pecans.
- Drizzle with balsamic glaze before serving.

Utensils needed:

Supplies: baking sheet, skillet, spoon, and cutting board.

- A knife

Recipe 14: Lemon-Dill Baked Cod with Steamed Asparagus

This light and tasty baked fish with a zesty lemon dill sauce is served with steamed asparagus, making it a low-fat and nutrient-dense dinner for persons with fatty livers. It's a simple yet lovely choice for a nutritious meal.

Ingredients List

- 4 cod fillets,
- 1 bunch trimmed asparagus,
- 2 tablespoons olive oil,
- 2 tablespoons fresh lemon juice,
- 1 tablespoon chopped dill,
- 2 cloves minced garlic.
- Salt and pepper to taste.
- Garnish with lemon slices.

The number of servings is four.

Procedure:

1. Preheat your oven to 400°F (200°C).
2. Place the fish fillets on a baking sheet. Arrange the asparagus around the fillets.
3. In a small bowl, combine the olive oil, lemon juice, dill, minced garlic, salt, and pepper.
4. Drizzle the lemon-dill mixture over the fish and asparagus.
5. Bake for 15-20 minutes, or until the cod flaked easily with a fork and the asparagus was soft.
6. Finish with lemon slices before serving.

Features and Variations:

➢ Replace cod with another white fish, such as tilapia or haddock.
➢ For a dash of spiciness, add a sprinkle of red pepper flakes.
➢ Serve over quinoa or brown rice.

Utensils needed: Baking sheet, small basin, whisk, and cutting board.

- A knife

Recipe 15: Vegetarian Turkey Meatballs with Zoodles

These turkey meatballs, stuffed with veggies and served over zoodles (zucchini noodles), provide a nutritional twist to a popular dish. This meal has plenty of lean protein and veggies, making it ideal for a fatty liver diet.

Ingredients List

- 1 pound ground turkey,
- 1 grated zucchini,
- 1 grated carrot,
- 1/2 cup breadcrumbs.
- 1/4 cup grated parmesan cheese.
- 1 egg
- 2 garlic cloves, minced
- One teaspoon of Italian seasoning.
- Salt and pepper to taste.
- 4 zucchinis spiralized into noodles.
- Marinara sauce to serve.

The number of servings is four.

Procedure:

1. Preheat your oven to 375°F (190°C).
2. In a mixing bowl, combine the ground turkey, shredded zucchini and carrot, breadcrumbs, Parmesan cheese, egg, chopped garlic, Italian seasoning, salt, and pepper.
3. Form the mixture into meatballs and place on a baking sheet.
4. Bake the meatballs for 20-25 minutes, or until well done.
5. In a pan, sauté the zoodles until soft.
6. To serve, top turkey meatballs with marinara sauce and zoodles.

Features and Variations:

➢ For extra greens, add chopped spinach or kale to the meatball mixture.
➢ Use whole-grain breadcrumbs to boost fiber.
➢ Garnish with fresh basil or parsley before serving.

Utensils needed: To prepare, you'll need a baking sheet, bowl, grater, spiralizer, skillet, and spoon.

Recipe #16: Chickpea and Spinach Stew

This hearty chickpea and spinach stew is a fiber-rich, plant-based choice for those aiming to improve liver function. It's a tasty and healthful option that has protein from chickpeas and a variety of veggies.

Ingredients List

- Two cans (15 ounces each) Chickpeas, drained and washed.
- Dice one onion.
- Mince three garlic cloves.
- One can (14 ounces) of chopped tomatoes
- 4 cups vegetable broth,
- 4 cups fresh spinach,
- 2 teaspoons ground cumin,
- 1 teaspoon smoky paprika.
- Salt and pepper to taste.
- 2 tablespoons olive oil.

Number of servings: 6

Procedure:

1. In a large saucepan, cook the onions and garlic in olive oil until tender.
2. Combine the chickpeas, diced tomatoes, vegetable broth, cumin, smoky paprika, salt, and pepper.
3. Bring the stew to a boil, then let it cook for 15-20 minutes.
4. Stir in the fresh spinach and simmer until wilted.
5. Adjust the seasoning as needed and serve warm.

Features and Variations:

➢ For added brightness, pour in more lemon juice.
➢ Garnish with fresh parsley or cilantro.
➢ Serve over brown rice or quinoa to complete the meal.

Utensils needed: large saucepan, wooden spoon, cutting board, and knife.

Recipe 17: Seared Tofu Stir-Fry with Broccoli and Snow Peas

This plant-based stir-fry with seared tofu and colorful veggies is a nutrient-dense addition to a fatty liver diet. Tofu serves as a protein-rich basis, with broccoli and snow peas adding color and fiber.

Ingredients List

- 1 pressed and diced block of extra-firm tofu,
- 2 cups broccoli florets.
- 1 cup trimmed snow peas,
- 1 julienned carrot,
- 3 teaspoons of soy sauce.
- 1 tablespoon sesame oil,
- 2 tablespoons rice vinegar,
- 1 tablespoon maple syrup,
- 1 teaspoon grated ginger,
- 2 chopped garlic cloves.
- Two teaspoons of vegetable oil.
- Sesame seeds as garnish

The number of servings is four.

Procedure:

1. In a large skillet, heat the vegetable oil over medium-high heat.
2. Add the cubed tofu and fry until golden brown on all sides.
3. Place the broccoli, snow peas, and julienned carrot in the skillet. Stir-fry for about 4-5 minutes, or until the veggies are soft and crisp.
4. In a bowl, combine soy sauce, sesame oil, rice vinegar, maple syrup, grated ginger, and chopped garlic.
5. Pour the sauce over the tofu and veggies and toss to cover evenly.
6. Sprinkle with sesame seeds and serve over brown rice or quinoa.

Features and Variations:

➢ Include your favorite vegetables, such as bell peppers or mushrooms.
➢ Taste and adjust the sweetness or saltiness accordingly.
➢ Add sliced green onions for added taste.

Utensils needed: large skillet, spatula, bowl, whisk, cutting board, and knife.

Recipe 18: Spaghetti Squash with Turkey Bolognese Sauce.

This lighter alternative to conventional spaghetti with meat sauce combines spaghetti squash with a savory turkey bolognese. It's a tasty, low-carb alternative that complements a fatty liver diet.

Ingredients List

- 1 large spaghetti squash, split and seeds removed
- 1 pound ground turkey
- 1 diced onion
- 2 minced garlic cloves
- 1 can (14 oz) crushed tomatoes,
- 1 teaspoon dried oregano,
- 1 teaspoon dried basil,
- Salt and pepper to taste,
- Fresh parsley for garnish,
- Grated Parmesan cheese for serving.

The number of servings is four.

Procedure:

1. Preheat your oven to 375°F (190°C).
2. Place the spaghetti squash halves on a baking pan, cut side down. Bake for 40–45 minutes, or until soft.
3. In a skillet, brown the ground turkey. Cook the chopped onions and minced garlic until softened.
4. Mix in the smashed tomatoes, oregano, basil, salt, and pepper. Simmer for 15–20 minutes.
5. With a fork, scrape the cooked spaghetti squash into "noodles".
6. Serve the turkey bolognese sauce over spaghetti squash. Garnish with fresh parsley and grated Parmigiano.

Features and Variations:

➢ Season the sauce with chopped bell peppers or mushrooms.
➢ Replace ground turkey with leaner ground chicken or beef.
➢ To add a little fire, sprinkle with red pepper flakes.

Utensils needed: baking sheet, skillet, fork, and cutting board.

- A knife

Recipe 19: Quinoa and Vegetable Stir-Fry.

This colorful quinoa and vegetable stir-fry is a healthy and filling choice for individuals concerned about their fatty liver. It's a simple and tasty meal option that includes bright vegetables and protein-rich quinoa.

Ingredients List

- 1 cup washed quinoa.
- 2 cups vegetable broth,
- 1 tablespoon oil,
- Thinly sliced onion,
- Thinly sliced bell pepper (any color),
- Julienned zucchini, julienned carrot, and clipped snap peas.
- Three teaspoons of soy sauce.
- 1 tablespoon rice vinegar,
- 1 teaspoon sesame oil,
- 1 teaspoon grated ginger,
- 2 chopped garlic cloves.
- Sesame seeds as garnish

The number of servings is four.

Procedure:

1. In a saucepan, heat the vegetable broth until it boils. Add the quinoa, decrease the heat, cover, and cook for 15 minutes, or until done.
2. Heat the vegetable oil in a large pan over medium-high heat.
3. Combine the cut onion, bell pepper, zucchini, carrot, and snap peas. Stir-fry the veggies for 5-7 minutes, or until soft and crisp.
4. In a small bowl, combine soy sauce, rice vinegar, sesame oil, grated ginger, and chopped garlic.
5. Pour the sauce over the cooked quinoa and veggies in the pan. Toss to blend.
6. Just before serving, garnish with sesame seeds.

Features and Variations:

➤ Add your favorite stir-fry veggies.
➤ Add tofu or edamame for extra protein.
➤ Serve with Sriracha for a spicy kick.

Utensils needed: A knife saucepan, skillet, wooden spoon, and cutting board.

Chapter 5: Snack Time Treats
Recipe #1: Avocado and Black Bean Salsa

This delicious Avocado and Black Bean Salsa is a nutrient-dense snack ideal for a fatty liver diet. It's a tasty alternative for guilt-free eating, packed with healthy fats, fiber, and antioxidants.

Ingredients List

- 2 avocados, diced
- One can (15 oz) of black beans, drained and rinsed
- 1 cup cherry tomatoes, chopped
- 1/2 red onion, coarsely diced
- 1 jalapeño, seeded and minced
- 1/4 cup fresh cilantro, chopped
- 2 teaspoons of lime juice.
- Salt and pepper to taste.
- Whole grain tortilla chips.

The number of servings is four.

Procedure:

1. In a large bowl, mix together diced avocados, black beans, cherry tomatoes, red onion, jalapeño, and cilantro.
2. Drizzle the lime juice over the mixture and toss lightly to incorporate.
3. Add salt and pepper to taste.
4. Serve with whole grain tortilla chips.

Features and Variations:

➢ For more spice, add a dash of cayenne pepper.
➢ Add chopped mango or pineapple for a tropical touch.
➢ To add brightness, squeeze in more lime juice before serving.

Utensils needed:

- Mixing bowl and spoon.

Recipe #2: Greek Yogurt and Berry Parfait

This Greek Yogurt and Berry Parfait is a delightful and protein-rich snack that's good for your liver. It's a delicious dessert that's high in antioxidants from mixed berries and Greek yogurt.

Ingredients List

- Two cups of Greek yogurt.
- One cup of mixed berries (strawberries, blueberries, raspberries)
- 2 tablespoons honey,
- 1/4 cup granola.
- Mint leaves as garnish (optional)

Number of servings: 2

Procedure:

1. In serving glasses or bowls, layer the Greek yogurt, mixed berries, and granola.
2. Drizzle the honey over each layer.
3. Repeat the layers until the glass is full.
4. Finish with a drizzle of honey and, if preferred, mint leaves.

Features and Variations:

➢ Plain Greek yogurt is a lower-sugar choice.
➢ Experiment with various berries or sliced bananas.
➢ For further variation, try flavored granola.

Utensils needed:

- Serve in glasses or bowls with a spoon.

Recipe #3: Roasted Chickpeas with Mediterranean Spices

These Roasted Chickpeas with Mediterranean Spices are a crisp and pleasant snack that is compatible with a fatty liver diet. These tasty chickpeas are packed with fiber and protein, making them ideal for snacking on the go.

Ingredients List

- 2 cans (15 oz) of chickpeas, rinsed and patted dry.
- 2 tablespoons olive oil,
- 1 teaspoon ground cumin,
- 1 teaspoon smoked paprika.
- One-half teaspoon garlic powder
- One-half teaspoon onion powder
- Salt to taste.

The number of servings is four.

Procedure:

1. Preheat your oven to 400°F (200°C).
2. In a bowl, combine chickpeas with olive oil, ground cumin, smoked paprika, garlic powder, onion powder, and salt.
3. Spread the chickpeas in a single layer on a baking sheet.
4. Roast for 25-30 minutes, or until the chickpeas are crispy, shaking halfway through.
5. Let cool before serving.

Features and Variations:

➢ For a spicy kick, season with a pinch of cayenne pepper.
➢ Experiment with various spice blends, such as curry or taco seasoning.
➢ Store in an airtight container for a quick snack.

Utensils needed:

Baking sheet, bowl, and spoon.

Recipe #4: Cucumber and Hummus Bites

These Cucumber and Hummus Bites are a light and pleasant snack choice for people looking to improve their liver health. The sharpness of the cucumber combined with the creaminess of the hummus results in a delicious and healthful meal.

Ingredients List

- One big cucumber, cut into rounds
- 1 cup hummus
- Cherry tomatoes as garnish
- Fresh dill as garnish

The number of servings is four.

Procedure:

1. Arrange cucumber rounds on a serving dish.
2. Spoon a tiny dollop of hummus onto each cucumber slice.
3. Top with a cherry tomato and garnish with fresh dill.

Features and Variations:

- Use flavored hummus for added diversity.

- To add texture, sprinkle with sesame seeds or pine nuts.

- Experiment with different herbs as garnish.

Utensils needed:

- Serve with a platter and spoon.

Recipe #5: Baked Apple Chips

These Baked Apple Chips provide a sweet and crunchy snack option that is compatible with a fatty liver diet. They are naturally sweetened and simple to prepare, making them a healthier option for satisfying your sweet tooth.

Ingredients List

- 2 apples
- 1 tablespoon cinnamon.
- One tablespoon of granulated sugar (optional)

Number of servings: 2

Procedure:

1. Preheat your oven to 200°F (95°C).
2. Toss apple slices with cinnamon and sugar (optional).
3. Place the apple slices in a single layer on a baking sheet lined with parchment paper.
4. Bake the apples for 2-3 hours, or until crisp, flipping halfway through.
5. Let cool before serving.

Features and Variations:

➤ Experiment with various apple kinds to create unique tastes.
➤ To add extra warmth, sprinkle with nutmeg or cardamom.
➤ To maintain crispiness, store in an airtight container.

Utensils needed:

- Baking sheet and parchment paper.

Recipe #6: Edamame and Sea Salt Snack Bowl

This Edamame and Sea Salt Snack Bowl is a protein-rich and savory choice for a fatty liver-friendly diet. Edamame is a good source of plant-based protein, and sea salt adds a satisfying flavor.

Ingredients List

- 2 cups frozen edamame, thawed

- 1 tablespoon olive oil

- Sea salt to taste

The number of servings is four.

Procedure:

1. Preheat your oven to 375°F (190°C).

2. Toss thawed edamame with olive oil and spread on a baking sheet.

3. Roast for 15-20 minutes or until edamame is slightly crispy.

4. Sprinkle with sea salt to taste.

5. Allow to cool before serving.

Features and Variations:

- Experiment with flavored sea salts to provide variation.

- To add a zesty touch, pour in some lemon juice.

- Serve as a snack or appetizer during parties.

Utensils needed: baking sheet, bowl, and spoon.

Recipe 7: Almond and Chia Seed Energy Bites

These Almond and Chia Seed Energy Bites are a nutritious and energy-boosting snack for folks battling fatty liver conditions. Packed with almonds, chia seeds, and a hint of sweetness, they give a handy and healthful choice.

Ingredients List

- 1 cup almonds, coarsely chopped
- 1/2 cup chia seeds
- 1/3 cup almond butter
- 1/4 cup honey
- 1 teaspoon vanilla extract
- Pinch of salt
- Shredded coconut for coating (optional)

Number of Servings: 12

Procedure:

1. In a dish, add chopped almonds, chia seeds, almond butter, honey, vanilla essence, and a sprinkle of salt.
2. Mix until completely incorporated.
3. Scoop out tablespoon-sized amounts and shape them into balls.
4. Optional: roll the energy bites in shredded coconut.
5. Refrigerate for at least 30 minutes before serving.

Features and Variations:

➢ Instead of almond butter, use peanut butter or any other nut butter of your choosing.
➢ For added sweetness, mix with dark chocolate chips or dried fruit.
➢ Refrigerate for prolonged shelf life.

Utensils needed:

- Bowl - Spoon - Baking sheet (optional coconut rolling)

Recipe #8: Cottage Cheese and Pineapple Skewers

These Cottage Cheese and Pineapple Skewers are a tasty combination of sweet and creamy, making them an ideal snack for a fatty liver diet. Cottage cheese gives nutrition, while pineapple adds natural sweetness.

Ingredients List

- One cup cottage cheese.

- One cup of fresh pineapple, chopped

- Wooden skewers

The number of servings is four.

Procedure:

1. Thread alternate slices of cottage cheese and pineapple onto wooden skewers.
2. Continue until all skewers are constructed.
3. Refrigerate for a minimum of 15 minutes before serving.

Features and Variations:

- Drizzle with honey for extra sweetness.
- Experiment with other fruits, such as strawberries and grapes.
- Serve as a small dessert or snack.

Utensils needed:

Wooden skewers

Recipe 9: Quinoa and Vegetable Stuffed Mini Peppers

These Quinoa and Veggie Stuffed Mini Peppers are a tasty and nutritious snack alternative for folks with fatty liver issues. They are a pleasant bite-sized treat that is high in protein from quinoa and colorful veggies.

Ingredients List

- 1 cup cooked quinoa,
- 1 cup chopped mixed veggies (bell peppers, cherry tomatoes, corn),
- 1/4 cup crumbled feta cheese.
- 2 tablespoons olive oil,
- 1 tablespoon balsamic vinegar.
- Salt and pepper to taste.
- Bell peppers for filling.

Number of servings: 6

Procedure:

1. In a mixing bowl, combine cooked quinoa, diced veggies, feta cheese, olive oil, balsamic vinegar, salt, and pepper.
2. Cut small bell peppers in half and remove the seeds.
3. Fill each pepper half with the quinoa-vegetable mixture.
4. Place on a serving plate and chill until ready to serve.

Features and Variations:

➤ For added protein, mix in black beans or chickpeas.
➤ Season with your preferred herbs or spices.
➤ Serve cold as a snack or appetizer.

Utensils needed: bowl, spoon, and serving tray.

Recipe 11: Spinach and Artichoke Dip with Vegetable Sticks.

This lightened-up Spinach and Artichoke Dip is a creamy, delicious dip that is good for your liver. Paired with crisp vegetable sticks, it's a delightful way to enjoy a traditional dip without sacrificing flavor.

Ingredients List

- 1 cup frozen spinach (thawed and drained),
- 1 can (14 oz) artichoke hearts (drained and diced),
- 1 cup low-fat Greek yogurt.
- 1/2 cup mayonnaise.
- One cup of shredded mozzarella cheese
- 1/4 cup grated Parmesan cheese
- 2 minced garlic cloves
- Salt and pepper to taste
- Carrot, celery, and bell pepper sticks.

Number of servings: 6

Procedure:

1. Preheat your oven to 375°F (190°C).
2. In a mixing dish, add frozen spinach, chopped artichoke hearts, Greek yogurt, mayonnaise, mozzarella cheese, Parmesan cheese, minced garlic, salt, and pepper.
3. Pour the mixture into a baking dish and bake for 20 to 25 minutes, or until bubbling and brown.
4. Serve heated with different vegetable sticks.

Features and Variations:

➢ Use whole-grain pita chips instead of vegetable sticks.
➢ Add a splash of hot sauce for a spicy bite.
➢ Before serving, sprinkle the top with chopped fresh parsley.

Utensils needed: Baking dish, bowl, and spoon.

Recipe 12: Sweet Potato and Black Bean Nachos.

These Sweet Potato and Black Bean Nachos are a nutrient-dense take on a traditional snack. They are a tasty alternative for people trying to maintain their liver health, since they are high in fiber and taste.

Ingredients List

- Thinly slice two medium sweet potatoes.
- One can (15 oz) of black beans.
- 1 cup diced cherry tomatoes,
- 1/2 cup finely chopped red onion,
- 1 sliced jalapeño (optional).
- 1 cup shredded cheddar cheese,
- 1 tablespoon olive oil,
- 1 teaspoon ground cumin,
- 1 teaspoon chili powder.
- Salt and pepper to taste.
- Garnish with fresh cilantro.
- Whole grain tortilla chips.

The number of servings is four.

Procedure:

1. Preheat your oven to 400°F (200°C).
2. In a bowl, combine sweet potato slices, olive oil, ground cumin, chili powder, salt, and pepper.
3. Place the sweet potato slices in a single layer on a baking pan.
4. Bake for 15-20 minutes, until the sweet potatoes are soft.
5. Top sweet potato slices with black beans, cherry tomatoes, red onion, jalapeño (optional), and shredded cheddar cheese.
6. Return to the oven and bake for 10 more minutes, or until the cheese is melted and bubbling.
7. Top with fresh cilantro and serve alongside whole-grain tortilla chips.

Features and Variations:

➢ For an additional creamy texture, add sliced avocado or guacamole.
➢ Replace black beans with pinto or refried beans.
➢ Drizzle with lime juice before serving.

Utensils needed: baking sheet, bowl, and spoon.

Recipe 13: Smoked Salmon with Cucumber Bites

These Smoked Salmon and Cucumber Bites are an exquisite, omega-3-rich snack that is easy on the liver. With a burst of freshness, they're a great addition to your snack repertoire.

Ingredients List

- 1 cucumber cut into rounds.
- 4 ounces smoked salmon, chopped into tiny pieces.
- 1/4 cup cream cheese
- 1 tablespoon of fresh dill, chopped
- Lemon zest as garnish

The number of servings is four.

Procedure:

1. Spread a tiny quantity of cream cheese on each cucumber circle.

2. Finish with a slice of smoked salmon.

3. Sprinkle fresh dill over top and garnish with lemon zest.

4. Serve cold.

Features and Variations:

- Add capers for an added burst of flavor.

- Use flavored cream cheese, such as chives or garlic.

- Serve with whole-grain crackers for a more substantial snack.

Utensils needed:

- Serve with a plate and knife.

Recipe 14: Turmeric and Honey Roasted Nuts

These Turmeric and Honey Roasted Nuts are a crispy, antioxidant-rich snack ideal for people with fatty livers. They are a tasty treat that has the health of nuts as well as the anti-inflammatory qualities of turmeric.

Ingredients List

- 2 cups mixed nuts (almonds, walnuts, cashews),
- 1 tablespoon olive oil,
- 1 tablespoon honey,
- 1 teaspoon powdered turmeric.
- 1/2 teaspoon of ground cinnamon.
- 1/4 teaspoon of cayenne pepper (optional).
- Salt to taste.

Number of servings: 6

Procedure:

1. Preheat your oven to 325°F (163°C).
2. In a bowl, combine the mixed nuts, olive oil, honey, ground turmeric, ground cinnamon, cayenne pepper (if using), and salt.
3. Arrange the nuts in a single layer on a baking sheet.
4. Roast for 15-20 minutes, until golden brown, stirring halfway through.
5. Let cool before serving.

Features and Variations:

- Adjust the cayenne pepper to your desired amount of heat.

- After roasting, season with a pinch of sea salt.

- Keep in an airtight container to maintain freshness.

Utensils needed: baking sheet, bowl, and spoon.

Recipe 15: Tuna and Avocado Lettuce Wraps.

Tuna and Avocado Lettuce Wraps are a protein-rich, low-carb snack alternative for a fatty liver diet. Avocado's smoothness and tuna's lean protein combine to provide a delicious and healthful treat.

Ingredients List

- 1 can (5 oz) drained tuna.
- one avocado, mashed
- 1/4 cup finely chopped red onion,
- 1 celery stalk,
- 1 tablespoon mayonnaise.
- 1 teaspoon Dijon mustard
- Salt and pepper to taste
- Butter lettuce leaves for wrapping

The number of servings is four.

Procedure:

1. In a bowl, mix together the tuna, mashed avocado, red onion, celery, mayonnaise, Dijon mustard, salt, and pepper.
2. Mix until well incorporated.
3. Spoon the tuna-avocado mixture into butter lettuce leaves.
4. Fold the leaves into bundles.
5. Serve cold.

Features and Variations:

- For added brightness, pour in more lemon juice.

- Add sliced pickles for a tart flavor.

- To add extra freshness, top with cherry tomatoes or sliced radishes.

Recipe 16: Roasted Red Pepper and Walnut Dip

This Roasted Red Pepper and Walnut Dip is a rich and tasty addition to a fatty liver diet. It's a tasty dip for veggie sticks or whole-grain crackers, thanks to the heart-healthy walnuts and the sweet smokiness of roasted red peppers.

Ingredients List

- Two big red bell peppers
- One cup of walnuts.
- 2 cloves garlic.
- 2 tablespoons olive oil,
- 1 teaspoon ground cumin,
- 1/2 teaspoon smoky paprika.
- Salt and pepper to taste.
- Garnish with fresh parsley.

Number of servings: 6

Procedure:

1. In a food processor, mix together roasted red peppers, toasted walnuts, garlic, olive oil, ground cumin, smoked paprika, salt, and pepper.
2. Blend until smooth and creamy.
3. Place in a serving basin and garnish with fresh parsley.
4. Serve alongside veggie sticks or whole-grain crackers.

Features and Variations:

- For a dash of spiciness, add a pinch of cayenne pepper.

- Drizzle with balsamic glaze before serving.

- Refrigerate leftovers to use as a wonderful sandwich spread.

Utensils needed: food processor, serving basin, and knife.

Recipe #17: Greek Salad Skewers

These Greek Salad Skewers are a pleasant and nutrient-dense snack for people who have fatty livers. They're a tasty bite-sized version of the typical Greek salad tastes.

Ingredients List

- Tomatoes and cucumber
- Pitted Kalamata olives,
- Cubed Feta cheese,
- Olive oil,
- Lemon juice.
- Dry oregano.
- Salt and pepper to taste.
- Wooden skewers.

The number of servings is four.

Procedure:

1. Thread cherry tomatoes, cucumber slices, Kalamata olives, and feta cheese cubes on wooden skewers.
2. In a small dish, combine the olive oil, lemon juice, dried oregano, salt, and pepper.
3. Drizzle the dressing on the skewers before serving.

Features and Variations:

- For added color, use red onion or bell pepper.

- For extra diversity, try flavored feta cheese.

- Serve as a refreshing appetizer during parties.

Utensils needed: wooden skewers, a small basin, and a whisk.

Recipe 18: Cauliflower Buffalo Bites.

Cauliflower Buffalo Bites are a delicious and gratifying alternative to regular buffalo wings. With the benefits of cauliflower and a tasty buffalo sauce, they make for a pleasantly spicy snack.

Ingredients List

- One head of cauliflower, chopped into florets
- Half cup whole wheat flour
- One-half cup water
- One teaspoon of garlic powder.
- One-half teaspoon onion powder
- 1/2 teaspoon of smoked paprika.
- Add salt and pepper to taste.
- Use 1/2 cup buffalo sauce.
- Two tablespoons of melted butter or olive oil
- Ranch or blue cheese dressing for dipping.

The number of servings is four.

Procedure:

1. Preheat your oven to 450°F (230°C).
2. In a mixing bowl, combine whole wheat flour, water, garlic powder, onion powder, smoked paprika, salt, and pepper to make a batter.
3. Dip each cauliflower floret into the batter, coating equally, and transfer to a baking sheet.
4. Bake for 20-25 minutes or until golden brown and crispy.
5. In a separate dish, combine the buffalo sauce and melted butter or olive oil.
6. Toss the cooked cauliflower with the buffalo sauce mixture until well covered.
7. Serve with ranch or blue cheese dressing for dipping.

Features and Variations:

➤ Adjust the buffalo sauce to your desired degree of heat.
➤ Bake on a wire rack for an additional crispy finish.
➤ Garnish with chopped chives or celery leaves.

Utensils needed: baking sheet, bowl, and whisk.

Recipe 19: Zucchini and Goat Cheese Roll-Ups.

These Zucchini and Goat Cheese Roll-Ups are a light and elegant snack suitable for a fatty liver diet. With the freshness of zucchini and the creamy taste of goat cheese, they make an excellent finger snack.

Ingredients List

- 2 medium zucchini, finely cut lengthwise.
- 4 oz goat cheese,
- Fresh basil,
- 1 tablespoon olive oil,
- Balsamic glaze for drizzling,
- Salt and pepper to taste.

The number of servings is four.

Procedure:

1. Lay out the zucchini slices and sprinkle a thin layer of goat cheese on each one.
2. Add a fresh basil leaf on the top of the goat cheese.
3. Roll the zucchini slices and bind them with toothpicks.
4. Place the roll-ups on a serving plate.
5. Finish with an olive oil and balsamic glaze.
6. Add salt and pepper to taste.

Features and Variations:

- For added flavor, add a piece of sun-dried tomato.

- Try flavored goat cheese, such as garlic or herb-infused.

- Serve as an appetizer during parties.

Utensils needed:

- Toothpicks and serving plate.

Recipe 20: Mango-Black Bean Salsa Cups

These Mango and Black Bean Salsa Cups are a sweet and delicious snack alternative for people who have fatty livers. They're a tasty bite-sized delight with mango's tropical taste and black beans' protein content.

Ingredients List

- One mango
- Drain and rinse one can (15 oz) of black beans.
- 1/2 finely chopped red onion,
- 1/4 cup chopped fresh cilantro,
- 1 juiced lime.
- Salt and pepper to taste.
- Tortilla cups or a scoop.-shaped tortilla chips.

Number of servings: 6

Procedure:

1. In a mixing dish, add chopped mango, black beans, red onion, cilantro, lime juice, salt, and pepper.
2. Mix until well incorporated.
3. Transfer the salsa mixture to tortilla cups or scoop-shaped tortilla chips.
4. Serve immediately.

Features and Variations:

- For a creamy texture, add chopped avocado.

- Add some chopped jalapeño for a spicy kick.

- Before serving, garnish with additional cilantro.

Utensils needed: - Bowl - Spoon

Chapter 6: Decadent Desserts
Recipe #1: Baked Cinnamon Apple Slices

Enjoy the natural sweetness of baked cinnamon apple slices while maintaining a healthy fatty liver diet. This dish is a delicious way to fulfill your sweet desire while being healthy.

Ingredient list:

- Four medium-sized apples.
- One tablespoon lemon juice.
- One teaspoon of ground cinnamon
- One spoonful of honey (optional).
- 1 tablespoon of chopped walnuts (optional).

Number of servings: four

Procedure:

1. Preheat the oven to 375°F (190°C).
2. To keep the apple slices from browning, mix them in a large basin with lemon juice.
3. Place the apple slices on a baking sheet lined with parchment paper.
4. Sprinkle ground cinnamon evenly over the apple slices.
5. For more sweetness, drizzle honey over top (optional).
6. Bake for 20–25 minutes, or until the apples are soft.
7. Remove from the oven and top with chopped walnuts (optional).
8. Let it cool slightly before serving.

Features and Variations:

➤ For a more decadent version, top with Greek yogurt.
➤ Experiment with various apple kinds to create distinct tastes.
➤ Adjust the amount of honey to your preferred level of sweetness.
➤ A sprinkle of nutmeg or a splash of vanilla extract complements this recipe well.

Utensils needed include a baking sheet, parchment paper, and a large dish.

Recipe #2: Chia Seed Pudding with Berries

⬅————————————————————————➡

Enjoy a guilt-free dessert with this Chia Seed Pudding, high in omega-3 fatty acids. This delectable delicacy is ideal for persons with fatty liver disease.

⬅————————————————————————➡

Ingredients:

- 1/4 cup chia seeds,
- 1 cup unsweetened almond milk,
- 1 tablespoon honey or maple syrup.
- 1/2 teaspoon vanilla essence
- 1 cup mixed berries (strawberries, blueberries, raspberries).

Two servings.

Directions:

1. In a dish, combine chia seeds, almond milk, honey (or maple syrup), and vanilla essence.
2. Stir thoroughly and chill for at least 2 hours or overnight, enabling the chia seeds to absorb the liquid and form a pudding-like consistency.
3. Before serving, whisk the mixture to remove any clumps.
4. Transfer the chia seed pudding to serving glasses or bowls.
5. Top with a good portion of mixed berries.

Features and Variations:

- Adjust sweetness using honey or maple syrup.

- Experiment with other berries or add sliced almonds for texture.

- Replace almond milk with coconut milk to make a creamier pudding.

- Make a batch at the start of the week for an easy grab-and-go treat.

Utensils required are a bowl, a spoon, and a refrigerator-safe container.

Recipe #3: Grilled Pineapple with Mint

Enjoy the tropical flavor of grilled pineapple with a refreshing dash of mint. This dessert is not only a tasty treat, but it is also an excellent addition to a fatty liver diet.

Ingredient list:

- One medium pineapple, peeled, cored, and sliced into rings
- 1 tablespoon coconut oil
- 1 tablespoon chopped fresh mint.
- 1 teaspoon of lime zest (optional).

Number of servings: four

Procedure:

1. Preheat the grill or grill pan over medium-high heat.

2. Coat pineapple rings with coconut oil.

3. Grill pineapple for 2-3 minutes on each side, or until grill marks emerge.

4. Remove from the grill and transfer to a serving plate.

5. Sprinkle chopped mint over the grilled pineapple.

6. Optional: Zest lime over top for an added punch of flavor.

Features and Variations:

- Add a dollop of low-fat vanilla ice cream for a delicious touch.

- For a sweet and spicy taste, season with a touch of chili powder.

- Keep the grill grates well-oiled to prevent sticking.

Utensils needed: grill or grill pan, basting brush, and serving tray.

Recipe #4: Avocado Chocolate Mousse

Indulge this creamy and luscious Avocado Chocolate Mousse to satisfy your chocolate cravings. This dessert is an excellent choice for individuals following a fatty liver diet since it is high in healthy fats.

Ingredients:

- 2 ripe avocados
- 1/4 cup unsweetened chocolate powder.
- 1/4 cup honey or maple syrup.
- 1 teaspoon vanilla essence,
- Pinch of salt,
- Fresh berries for garnish.

Number of servings: four

Procedure:

1. In a blender or food processor, mix avocados, cocoa powder, honey (or maple syrup), vanilla extract, and salt.
2. Blend until smooth and creamy.
3. Spoon the chocolate mousse into the serving glasses.
4. Refrigerate for at least 30 minutes before serving.
5. Just before serving, garnish with fresh berries.

Features and Variations:

- Adjust sweetness using honey or maple syrup.

- To add texture, top with chopped nuts or shredded coconut.

- Finish with a sprinkling of sea salt for a sweet and salty contrast.

Utensils needed:

To prepare, use a blender or food processor, a spoon, and serving glasses.

Recipe #5: Lemon Blueberry Frozen Yogurt

Enjoy a delightful Lemon Blueberry Frozen Yogurt. This guilt-free dessert is ideal for individuals who want to manage their fatty liver while still enjoying a delicious treat.

Ingredient list:

- Two cups plain Greek yogurt.
- 1/4 cup honey, agave syrup
- Zest from 1 lemon
- One cup of fresh blueberries

Number of servings: four

Directions:

1. In a dish, add Greek yogurt, honey (or agave syrup), and lemon zest.
2. Gently fold in the fresh blueberries.
3. Place the mixture in an ice cream maker and churn according to the manufacturer's directions.
4. Once churned, place the frozen yogurt in a closed container and freeze for another 2 hours to firm up.
5. Scoop and serve with more blueberries on top.

Features and Variations:

➤ Experiment with various berries or a combination of berries to create unique flavors.
➤ Before serving, add granola for extra crunch.
➤ Let the frozen yogurt soften slightly before scooping for a creamier texture.

Utensils needed:

- Bowl - Ice cream maker.

- Lidded container.

Recipe 6: Baked Pear with Cinnamon and Almond

Serve roasted pears with cinnamon and almonds for a delicious dessert. This cozy dessert is an excellent addition to a fatty liver diet.

Ingredient list:

- 4 ripe pears (halved and cored)
- 1 teaspoon ground cinnamon
- 1/4 cup chopped almonds.
- 2 tablespoons honey
- 1 tablespoon lemon juice.

Number of servings: four

Procedure:

1. Preheat the oven to 375°F (190°C).

2. Put the pear halves on a baking dish, cut side up.

3. To avoid browning, drizzle lemon juice over the pears.

4. In a small dish, combine cinnamon and sliced almonds.

5. Sprinkle the cinnamon-almond mixture over each pear half.

6. Drizzle the honey evenly over the pears.

7. Bake for 25–30 minutes, or until the pears are soft.

8. Let cool slightly before serving.

Features and Variations:

➢ Enjoy with a scoop of low-fat whipped cream or Greek yogurt.
➢ Experiment with various pears to create a variety of tastes.
➢ A touch of nutmeg may give another layer of warmth to your dish.

Utensils needed include a baking dish, a small bowl, and a spoon.

Recipe #7: Coconut Chia Seed Pudding Parfait

Enjoy the tropical flavors of coconut in this Chia Seed Pudding Parfait. This dessert, made with layers of coconut-infused chia pudding and fresh fruit, is both delicious and beneficial for people who have fatty liver.

Ingredients:

- 1/4 cup chia seeds,
- 1 cup coconut milk,
- 2 tablespoons maple syrup,
- 1/2 teaspoon coconut essence,
- 1 cup mixed tropical fruits (pineapple, mango, kiwi).

Two servings.

Instructions:

1. In a bowl, mix chia seeds, coconut milk, maple syrup, and coconut essence.
2. Mix thoroughly and chill for at least 2 hours, or until a pudding-like consistency is reached.
3. Before serving, stack the coconut chia pudding with a variety of tropical fruits in serving glasses.
4. Add layers as desired.

Features and Variations:

- Top with toasted coconut flakes for texture.

- For a nutty twist, substitute almond milk for the coconut milk.

- Experiment with different tropical fruits to see what tastes best to you.

Utensils required are a bowl, a spoon, and a refrigerator-safe container.

Recipe #8: Mango and Basil Sorbet

Enjoy a refreshing handcrafted sorbet prepared with sweet mango and fragrant basil. This dairy-free, liver-friendly dessert is bursting with tropical flavors.

Ingredient list:

- 2 cups peeled and diced mango,
- 1/4 cup fresh basil,
- 1/4 cup honey or agave syrup.
- One tablespoon lime juice.

Number of servings: four

Procedure:

1. In a blender, mix chopped mango, fresh basil, honey (or agave syrup), and lime juice.
2. Blend until smooth.
3. Pour the mixture into an ice cream machine and churn according the manufacturer's directions.
4. Once churned, place the sorbet in a covered container and freeze for a further 2 hours.
5. Scoop and garnish with a sprig of fresh basil.

Features and Variations:

- Adjust sweetness using honey or agave syrup.

- For an added kick, add a pinch of cayenne pepper to the blender.

- Finish with more chopped mango for a delicious garnish.

Utensils needed:

Blender, ice cream machine, and lidded container.

Recipe #9: Raspberry Almond Bites

Enjoy these bite-sized snacks made with raspberries and almonds. These Raspberry Almond Bites are ideal for satisfying sweet cravings while keeping your fatty liver in check.

Ingredient list:

- 1 cup fresh raspberries,
- 1/2 cup almond flour,
- 2 tablespoons honey,
- 1/4 cup unsweetened shredded coconut.

Number of servings: six

Procedure:

1. In a food processor, blend fresh raspberries, almond flour, and honey.
2. Blend until the mixture has a dough-like consistency.
3. Scoop out tiny amounts and shape into bite-sized balls.
4. Roll the balls in shredded coconut until they are equally covered.
5. Transfer the Raspberry Almond Bites to a platter and chill for at least 30 minutes before serving.

Features and Variations:

- ➢ Add vanilla extract to increase flavor.
- ➢ Instead of coconut, wrap the bits in broken almonds to create a crispy surface.
- ➢ Keep in an airtight container in the refrigerator for maximum freshness.

Utensils required: - Food processor - Plate - Refrigerator-safe container.

Recipe 10: Cinnamon Walnut Stuffed Dates.

Indulge in naturally delicious and nutrient-rich Cinnamon Walnut Stuffed Dates. This simple yet gorgeous dessert is an excellent complement to your fatty liver diet.

Ingredients:

- 12 pitted Medjool dates,
- 1/4 cup chopped walnuts,
- 1 teaspoon ground cinnamon.
- 1 tablespoon almond butter, unsweetened

Number of servings: six

Instructions:

1. In a small dish, combine chopped walnuts and cinnamon.
2. Carefully split each date lengthwise to remove the pit.
3. Fill each date with a tiny quantity of walnut-cinnamon mixture.
4. Spread a spoonful of almond butter on each filled date.
5. Place the filled dates on a serving plate.

Features and Variations:

- Drizzle with honey for extra sweetness.

- Experiment with various nut butters to create unique tastes.

- Serve as a fast and nutritious snack or dessert choice.

Utensils needed:

Small bowl, knife, and platter.

Recipe 11: Pomegranate Yogurt Parfait.

Enjoy a boost of antioxidants with this Pomegranate Yogurt Parfait. Layers of creamy yogurt, crunchy granola, and vivid pomegranate seeds make this a delicious and liver-friendly dessert choice.

Ingredient list:

- Two cups plain Greek yogurt.
- 1/4 cup honey or maple syrup.
- 1 cup low-sugar granola
- 1 cup pomegranate seeds.

Number of servings: four

Procedure:

1. To prepare, layer Greek yogurt, honey or maple syrup, granola, and pomegranate seeds in a serving glass or dish.
2. Add layers as desired.
3. Finally, sprinkle pomegranate seeds on top.
4. Serve immediately and enjoy the cool parfait.

Features and Variations:

- Try flavored Greek yogurt for more diversity.

- To add additional warmth, sprinkle with cinnamon or nutmeg.

- For a different texture, mix broken nuts into the granola.

Utensils needed:

- Serve in glasses or bowls with a spoon.

Recipe 12: Almond Flour Banana Bread.

Enjoy this moist and tasty Almond Flour Banana Bread that is gluten-free and suited for a fatty liver diet. This healthful snack is ideal for savoring the familiar flavor of banana bread without jeopardizing your health.

Ingredients:

- 2 cups almond flour
- 1 teaspoon baking soda.
- 1/4 teaspoon of salt.
- Three ripe bananas, mashed
- 3 eggs
- 1/4 cup melted coconut oil.
- 1/4 cup honey or maple syrup.
- One teaspoon vanilla extract.

Number of servings: eight

Procedure:

1. Preheat oven to 350°F (175°C) and oil loaf pan.
2. In a large mixing basin, add almond flour, baking soda, and salt.
3. In a separate mixing dish, combine mashed bananas, eggs, melted coconut oil, honey (or maple syrup), and vanilla extract.
4. Mix the wet components with the dry ingredients until completely blended.
5. Transfer the batter to the oiled loaf pan.
6. Bake for 45–55 minutes, or until a toothpick inserted in the center comes out clean.
7. Let the banana bread cool before slicing.

Features and Variations:

➢ Add chopped nuts or dark chocolate chips for more taste.
➢ To add fiber, fold in shredded zucchini or carrots.
➢ Serve slices on their own or with a dollop of Greek yogurt.

Utensils needed include a loaf pan, mixing bowls, and a whisk.

Recipe 13: Mint Chocolate Avocado Popsicles.

Cool down with these Mint Chocolate Avocado Popsicles, a creamy and delicious treat. Avocado has a silky feel and complements the health-conscious tone of your fatty liver diet.

Ingredients:

- Two ripe avocados
- Half cup unsweetened almond milk
- 1/4 cup honey, agave syrup
- 1 teaspoon peppermint essence
- 2 tablespoons unsweetened cocoa powder.

Servings: 6 popsicles.

Procedure:

1. In a blender, mix avocados, almond milk, honey (or agave syrup), peppermint essence, and cocoa powder.
2. Blend until smooth and creamy.
3. Pour the mixture into the popsicle molds.
4. Insert the popsicle sticks and freeze for at least four hours, or until solid.
5. Run the molds under warm water to remove the popsicles.

Features and Variations:

➢ Experiment with different extracts such as vanilla or almond to create unique flavors.
➢ Include a handful of spinach for an extra nutritious boost.
➢ To add an additional delight, drizzle melted dark chocolate over the frozen popsicles.

To make popsicles, you'll need a blender, popsicle molds, and sticks.

Recipe 14: Cranberry-Orange Quinoa Pudding

Cranberry Orange Quinoa Pudding is a healthier alternative to regular rice pudding. This dessert is an excellent complement to your fatty liver diet, as it is high in fiber and antioxidants.

Ingredients:

- 1 cup cooked quinoa,
- 1 cup unsweetened almond milk,
- 1/4 cup honey or maple syrup.
- 1 teaspoon vanilla essence
- 1/2 cup dried cranberries.
- Zest from 1 orange

Number of servings: four

Procedure:

1. In a saucepan, mix cooked quinoa, almond milk, honey (or maple syrup), and vanilla essence.
2. Bring to a simmer over medium heat, stirring constantly.
3. Once simmering, decrease the heat to low and continue cooking until the sauce thickens (about 15-20 minutes).
4. Remove from heat and mix in the dried cranberries and orange zest.
5. Let the quinoa pudding cool before serving.

Features and Variations:

➢ Add a sprinkling of cinnamon for extra warmth.
➢ For a tart flavor, use fresh cranberries when they are in season.
➢ Serve warm or cold, according to your preferences.

Utensils needed:

- A saucepan and a stirring spoon.

Recipe 15. Blueberry Lemon Muffins with Oat Flour

Bake these Blueberry Lemon Muffins with Oat Flour for a guilt-free breakfast delight. These muffins are not only delicious, but they also support your fatty liver diet with their nutritious contents.

Ingredients:

- 2 cups oat flour
- 1 teaspoon baking powder.
- One-half teaspoon baking soda
- 1/4 teaspoon of salt.
- two ripe bananas, mashed
- 2 eggs
- 1/4 cup melted coconut oil.
- 1/4 cup honey or maple syrup.
- One teaspoon vanilla extract.
- Zest from 1 lemon
- One cup of fresh blueberries

Servings: 12 muffins.

Procedure:

1. 1: Preheat oven to 350°F (175°C) and line muffin tray with paper liners.
2. In a bowl, combine the oat flour, baking powder, baking soda, and salt.
3. In another dish, combine the mashed bananas, eggs, melted coconut oil, honey (or maple syrup), vanilla essence, and lemon zest.
4. Mix together the wet and dry ingredients, then gently fold in the fresh blueberries.
5. Spoon the batter into the muffin tray.
6. Bake for 18 to 22 minutes, or until a toothpick inserted in the middle comes out clean.
7. Let the muffins cool before serving.

Features and Variations:

➢ Add chopped nuts for added crunch.
➢ To provide diversity, substitute blueberries with other fruit.
➢ These muffins are an ideal on-the-go snack.

Utensils needed include a whisk, a muffin tray, paper liners, and mixing bowls.

Recipe #16: Chocolate Chia Seed Pudding

Enjoy Chocolate Chia Seed Pudding, a delectable dessert ideal for a fatty liver diet.

Ingredient list:

- 1/4 cup chia seeds,
- 1 cup unsweetened almond milk,
- 2 teaspoons chocolate powder.
- Two tablespoons of honey or maple syrup.
- 1/2 teaspoon of vanilla essence.
- Dark chocolate shavings as garnish (optional)

Two servings.

Instructions:

1. In a dish, mix chia seeds, almond milk, chocolate powder, honey (or maple syrup), and vanilla essence.
2. Whisk well to ensure that the ingredients are evenly distributed.
3. Refrigerate for at least 2 hours, preferably overnight, to allow the chia seeds to absorb the liquid.
4. Before serving, transfer the mixture and spoon to serving glasses.
5. Garnish with dark chocolate shavings for an added touch of decadence.

Features and Variations:

➢ Adjust sweetness using honey or maple syrup.
➢ Add a spoonful of whipped coconut cream for extra deliciousness.
➢ Experiment with other toppings, such as fresh berries or chopped almonds.

Utensils needed:

Bowl, whisk, and serving glasses.

Recipe #17: Turmeric Ginger Golden Milk Popsicles

Turmeric Ginger Golden Milk Popsicles are an anti-inflammatory twist on a popular delight. These popsicles are packed with health advantages and ideal for individuals on a fatty liver diet.

Ingredients:

- 1 cup unsweetened coconut milk,
- 1 teaspoon of turmeric,
- 1/2 teaspoon ground ginger,
- 2 tablespoons honey or agave syrup.
- A pinch of black pepper (improves turmeric absorption)

Servings: 6 popsicles.

Procedure:

1. Warm coconut milk in a pot over low heat.
2. Mix in the turmeric, ginger, honey (or agave syrup), and a dash of black pepper.
3. Whisk until well blended and warmed through.
4. Let the mixture cool before pouring into popsicle molds.
5. Freeze for at least four hours, or until solid.
6. Run the molds under warm water to remove the popsicles.

Features and Variations:

- Add lemon or lime juice for a zesty flavor.

- Experiment with coconut water or almond milk to create different tastes.

- For extra freshness, mix with finely chopped fresh mint.

Utensils needed include a saucepan, a whisk, and popsicle molds.

Recipe 18: Cauliflower Chocolate Muffins.

Cauliflower Chocolate Muffins are a fun way to sneak veggies into your dessert. These moist and chocolaty sweets are a guilt-free joy for people concerned about their fatty liver condition.

Ingredients:

- 2 cups cooked cauliflower florets
- 2 ripe bananas, mashed
- 3 eggs
- 1/4 cup melted coconut oil.
- 1/4 cup honey or maple syrup,
- 1 teaspoon vanilla essence,
- 1/3 cup chocolate powder.
- One-half teaspoon baking powder
- 1/4 teaspoon of salt.
- Dark chocolate chips for the topping (optional)

Servings: 12 muffins.

Procedure:

1. Preheat oven to 350°F (175°C) and line muffin tray with paper liners.
2. In a blender, mix cauliflower, bananas, eggs, melted coconut oil, honey (or maple syrup), and vanilla extract. Blend until smooth.
3. In a separate basin, mix together the cocoa powder, baking powder, and salt.
4. Mix the wet and dry ingredients until fully combined.
5. Spoon the batter into the muffin tray, then sprinkle with dark chocolate chips if preferred.
6. Bake for 18 to 22 minutes, or until a toothpick inserted in the middle comes out clean.
7. Let the muffins cool before serving.

Features and Variations:

➢ Add chopped nuts for texture.
➢ Make sure the cauliflower is thoroughly cooked and mashed for a smooth consistency.
➢ These muffins make a great snack or morning treat.

Utensils needed include a muffin tin, paper liners, a blender, and mixing bowls.

Recipe #19: Vanilla Matcha Green Tea Smoothie Bowl

Indulge in a visually appealing and healthful Vanilla Matcha Green Tea Smoothie Bowl. This bowl is packed with antioxidants and taste, and it's a great way to end a meal on a healthy note.

Ingredients:

- 2 frozen bananas,
- 1 cup spinach leaves,
- 1/2 cup plain Greek yogurt.
- One teaspoon matcha green tea powder.
- 1/2 teaspoon vanilla extract
- Fresh berries, sliced kiwi, granola, and chia seeds.

Two servings.

Procedure:

1. In a blender, mix frozen bananas, spinach, Greek yogurt, matcha powder, and vanilla essence.
2. Blend until smooth and creamy.
3. Pour the smoothie into bowls and garnish with fresh berries, sliced kiwi, granola, and chia seeds.
4. Serve immediately and eat with a spoon.

Features and Variations:

➢ Optional: Add honey or maple syrup to adjust sweetness.
➢ Experiment with other toppings such as crushed coconut and sliced almonds.
➢ Feel free to personalize the bowl with your preferred fruits and nuts.

Utensils needed:

Blender, bowl, and spoon.

Recipe 20: Walnut and Date Energy Bites.

Nutritious Walnut and Date Energy Bites satisfy your sweet needs. These bite-sized sweets are not only delicious, but also a healthy choice for people on a fatty liver diet.

Ingredients:

- 1 cup walnuts
- 1 cup pitted dates.
- 1 tablespoon chia seeds,
- 1 teaspoon cinnamon,
- A pinch of salt,
- Optional unsweetened shredded coconut for rolling.

Servings: 12-15 nibbles.

Procedure:

1. In a food processor, blend walnuts, dates, chia seeds, cinnamon, and salt.
2. Pulse the ingredients until they form a sticky dough.
3. Scoop out tiny amounts and shape into bite-sized balls.
4. To add texture, roll the energy bites in shredded coconut.
5. Refrigerate for at least 30 minutes before serving.

Features and Variations:

- Add a scoop of protein powder for an additional protein boost.

- Add a handful of dark chocolate chips for a hint of sweetness.

- Keep in an airtight container in the refrigerator for maximum freshness.

Utensils needed:

Required items: food processor, spoon, and refrigerator-safe container.

Enjoy these variety and nutritious dessert alternatives, each carefully designed to complement a fatty liver diet while providing delicious tastes.

Chapter 7: Smoothie
1. Berry Blast Smoothie.

This antioxidant-rich smoothie is a delicious combination of berries designed specifically for folks with a fatty liver. Berries are recognized for their anti-inflammatory effects, making this a tasty and healthful option.

Ingredients:

- 1 cup of mixed berries (blueberries, strawberries, raspberries)
- 1/2 banana
- Half cup Greek yogurt
- One spoonful of chia seeds
- One cup unsweetened almond milk.

Two servings.

Instructions:

1. Blend berries, banana, Greek yogurt, chia seeds, and almond milk.

2. Blend until smooth and creamy.

3. Pour into cups and drink immediately.

Features and Variations:

- Add spinach for additional nutrients.

- Frozen berries provide a cooler, thicker texture.

- To adjust the sweetness, add honey or stevia as needed.

Utensils needed:

A blender

2. Green Revitalizing Smoothie.

This smoothie is a liver-loving powerhouse, thanks to its cleansing greens content. Ideal for people wishing to begin their road toward a healthy liver.

Ingredients:

- 1 cup kale (stems removed)
- 1/2 chopped cucumber
- 1/2 cored green apple
- 1/2 juiced lemon
- One spoonful of flaxseeds
- One cup coconut water.

Two servings.

Instructions:

1. Blend kale, cucumber, green apple, lemon juice, flaxseeds, and coconut water.
2. Blend until smooth and vivid.
3. Pour into glasses and savor the green delight.

Features and Variations:

- Add a knob of ginger for a spicy kick.

- Experiment with other greens, such as spinach and Swiss chard.

- Adjust the thickness by adding additional coconut water as needed.

Utensils needed:

A blender

3. Tropical Turmeric Delight.

Enjoy the anti-inflammatory properties of turmeric in this tropical-inspired smoothie. A rush of exotic tastes that are mild on the liver.

Ingredient list:

- One cup of pineapple pieces
- 1/2 mango, peeled and diced
- 1 teaspoon turmeric powder
- One spoonful of hemp seeds
- One cup coconut milk.

Two servings.

Instructions:

1. Blend pineapple, mango, turmeric powder, hemp seeds, and coconut milk.

2. Process till smooth and tropical sunshine yellow.

3. Pour into glasses and enjoy the unusual tastes.

Features and Variations:

- Add a sprinkle of black pepper for better turmeric absorption.

- Freeze the pineapple to create a frosty effect.

- If desired, adjust the sweetness with a little amount of agave syrup.

Utensils needed:

- A blender

4. Citrus Detox Elixir

This delightful cleansing elixir will give your liver a zesty boost. It's a spicy and energizing choice for liver health, thanks to its high vitamin C content.

Ingredients:

- 1 orange, peeled and segments
- Peel and slice
- 1/2 grapefruit.
- Juice 1/2 lime.
- 1 tablespoon mint leaves,
- 1 cup water.

Two servings.

Procedure:

1. In a blender, mix orange, grapefruit, lime juice, mint leaves, and water.
2. Process until refreshing and citrusy.
3. Pour into glasses and taste the zing.

Features and Variations:

- To make a cold beverage, add ice.

- Experiment with various citrus fruits, such as lemon and tangerine.

- Add more mint leaves for a blast of freshness.

Utensils needed:

- A blender

5. Creamy avocado delight.

Enjoy the creamy richness of avocado while improving your liver health. This smoothie is a silky combination that will satisfy your taste senses while also nourishing your body.

Ingredient list:

- 1 peeled and pitted avocado,
- 1/2 cup spinach,
- 1/2 banana.
- One spoonful of almond butter.
- One cup almond milk.

Two servings.

Procedure:

1. Blend avocado, spinach, banana, almond butter, and almond milk.

2. Blend until smooth and creamy.

3. Pour into glasses and enjoy the smooth texture.

Features and Variations:

- Add vanilla extract for more taste.

- Use frozen banana to achieve a thicker consistency.

- Sprinkle with sliced almonds for a crisp touch.

Utensils needed:

- Blender

6. Beetroot Bliss Smoothie.

This bright and nutrient-dense smoothie takes use of beets' cleansing properties. A lovely method to promote liver health while indulging in earthy tastes.

Ingredients:

- 1 small sliced beet
- 1/2 cup mixed berries (blueberries, raspberries)
- 1/2 cup Greek yogurt.
- 1 tablespoon honey
- 1 cup water.

Two servings.

Instructions:

1. Blend chopped beet, mixed berries, Greek yogurt, honey, and water.

2. Blend until smooth and brightly colored.

3. Pour into glasses and enjoy the beetroot delight.

Features and Variations:

- Add lemon juice for a zesty flavor.

- If necessary, add more honey to adjust the sweetness.

- Garnish with fresh mint leaves for a punch of flavor.

Utensils needed:

- A blender

7. Pineapple Ginger Soother.

The anti-inflammatory qualities of ginger in this delicious pineapple smoothie can help with digestion and liver health. A tropical elixir with a touch of spiciness.

Ingredient list:

- One cup of pineapple pieces
- 1 teaspoon grated ginger
- 1/2 banana.
- One spoonful of chia seeds
- One cup coconut water.

Two servings.

Instructions:

1. Blend pineapple chunks, grated ginger, banana, chia seeds, and coconut water.
2. Blend until smooth and refreshing.
3. Pour into glasses and enjoy the calming combination of pineapple and ginger.

Features and Variations:

- Add a sprinkle of turmeric for additional anti-inflammatory effects.

- If necessary, add additional coconut water to get the required thickness.

- Finish with a pineapple slice for a tropical touch.

Utensils needed:

- A blender

8. Cucumber-Mint Cooler

This delicious cucumber mint smoothie will keep you hydrated and help your liver. This refreshing combination is ideal for hot days or as a post-workout treat.

Ingredients:

- 1/2 peeled and sliced cucumber
- 1 cup spinach leaves
- 1/2 cup mint leaves.
- 1/2 cored green apple
- 1 cup coconut water.

Two servings.

Instructions:

1. Blend cucumber slices, spinach leaves, mint leaves, green apple, and coconut water.
2. Blend until smooth and revitalized.
3. Pour into glasses and enjoy the crisp, refreshing sensation.

Features and Variations:

- Add lime juice for a zesty flavor.

- Experiment with several types of mint.

- Add cucumber slices for enhanced visual appeal.

Utensils needed:

- A blender

9. Gold Glow Turmeric Smoothie

Enjoy the golden hues of this turmeric-infused smoothie, which is intended to give anti-inflammatory assistance for your liver. A cheerful and nourishing treat.

Ingredient list:

- One banana.

- 1/2 cup mango chunks.

- One teaspoon of turmeric powder.

- One spoonful of flaxseeds

- One cup almond milk.

        Two servings.

Procedure:

1. Blend banana, mango chunks, turmeric powder, flaxseeds, and almond milk.
2. Blend until smooth and golden.
3. Pour into glasses and enjoy the brilliant glow of this turmeric pleasure.

Features and Variations:

- Add a sprinkle of cinnamon for warming.

- If desired, adjust the sweetness with a small amount of maple syrup.

- Add a sprinkle of turmeric for visual appeal.

Utensils needed:

- A blender

10. Blueberry Basil Infusion.

The unusual blend of blueberries and basil will elevate your smoothie experience. This antioxidant-rich combination is both refreshing and healthy, and it promotes liver function.

Ingredients:

- 1 cup blueberries,
- 1/2 cup fresh basil leaves,
- 1/2 banana.
- One spoonful of hemp seeds
- 1 cup water.

Two servings.

Procedure:

1. In a blender, add blueberries, basil leaves, banana, hemp seeds, and water.
2. Blend until smooth and fragrant.
3. Pour into glasses and enjoy the flavorful combination of blueberries and basil.

Features and Variations:

- Add lime juice for a zesty flavor.

- Try frozen blueberries for a colder texture.

- Add a basil leaf for a final touch.

Utensils required: - Blender

11. Almond Joy Smoothie

Enjoy the delectable blend of almonds and coconut in this creamy and delightful smoothie. It's a delicious treat for your taste buds and liver, full of healthy fats and a hint of sweetness.

Ingredient list:

- 1/2 cup almonds overnight.

- 1 frozen banana.

- 2 tablespoons of unsweetened shredded coconut.

- One spoonful of cacao powder.

- One cup almond milk.

Two servings.

Instructions:

1. Blend soaked almonds, frozen banana, shredded coconut, cacao powder, and almond milk.
2. Blend until creamy and delicious.
3. Pour into glasses and enjoy the nutty delight.

Features and Variations:

- Add a dab of almond butter for added richness.

- If preferred, add a little of honey or maple syrup to adjust the sweetness.

- Add a sprinkling of shredded coconut for visual appeal.

Utensils needed:

- A blender

12. Spinach Pineapple Paradise.

This spinach and pineapple smoothie will transport you to a tropical paradise. It's a refreshing choice for boosting liver function, as it's high in vitamins and minerals.

Ingredients:

- 2 cups fresh spinach leaves
- 1 cup pineapple pieces.
- 1/2 peeled and sliced cucumber,
- 1 tablespoon chia seeds.
- One cup coconut water.

Two servings.

Instructions:

1. Blend spinach, pineapple, cucumber, chia seeds, and coconut water.

2. Blend until smooth and tropical-green.

3. Pour into glasses and enjoy the taste of heaven.

Features and Variations:

- Add ice for a cooled experience.

- Experiment with other greens, such as kale and Swiss chard.

- Add a pineapple slice for a decorative accent.

Utensils needed:

- A blender

13. Mango Ginger Refresher.

Indulge your senses with this energizing mango and ginger smoothie. The mix of sweet mango and spicy ginger produces a pleasant flavor that is not only delicious but also good for your liver.

Ingredient list:

- 1 cup mango chunks,
- 1 teaspoon grated ginger,
- 1/2 banana
- One spoonful of hemp seeds
- 1 cup water.

Two servings.

Instructions:

1. Blend mango chunks, grated ginger, banana, hemp seeds, and water.

2. Process until smooth and delightfully unique.

3. Pour into glasses and enjoy your tropical fusion.

Features and Variations:

- Add lime juice for a zesty flavor.

- If desired, adjust the sweetness with a little amount of agave syrup.

- Garnish with a piece of fresh mango for an additional touch.

Utensils needed:

- A blender

14. Raspberry Lemonade Smoothie.

Enjoy the tangy taste of raspberry lemonade in a nutritious smoothie. This cool combination is a delicious variation on a popular summer beverage that is great for your liver.

Ingredient list:

- 1 cup raspberries

- 1/2 lemon (juiced)

- One-half banana

- One spoonful of flaxseeds

- One cup coconut water.

Two servings.

Procedure:

1. Blend raspberries, lemon juice, banana, flaxseeds, and coconut water.

2. Blend until smooth and evocative of a summer's day.

3. Pour into glasses and enjoy the raspberry lemonade delight.

Features and Variations:

- To make a cold beverage, add ice.

- If preferred, add a little of honey to adjust the sweetness.

- Add a lemon slice as a decorative accent.

Utensils needed:

- A blender

15. Cherry Almond Dream.

This smoothie is a beautiful combination of cherries and almonds. It's a delicious choice for individuals looking for a sweet and nutritional treat, thanks to its high antioxidant content and healthy fats.

Ingredients:

- 1 cup pitted cherries,
- 1/2 cup soaked almonds,
- 1/2 banana.
- 1 tablespoon honey, 1 cup almond milk.

Two servings.

Procedure:

1. Blend pitted cherries, soaked almonds, banana, honey, and almond milk.

2. Blend until smooth and silky.

3. Pour into glasses and enjoy the cherry almond fantasy.

Features and Variations:

- Add a sprinkle of cinnamon for warming.

- If necessary, add more honey to adjust the sweetness.

- Add a cherry on top for a beautiful touch.

Utensils required: - Blender

16. Peach Basil Bliss

Enhance your smoothie experience with the delectable blend of sweet peaches and fragrant basil. This smoothie is a delicious symphony of tastes that will help your liver health.

Ingredients:

- 1 cup sliced peaches.

- 1/2 cup fresh basil leaves.

- One-half banana

- One spoonful of chia seeds

- One cup coconut water.

Two servings.

Instructions:

1. Blend sliced peaches, basil leaves, banana, chia seeds, and coconut water.

2. Puree until smooth and pleasantly peachy.

3. Pour into glasses and savor the delicious mixture.

Features and Variations:

- Add lime juice for a zesty flavor.

- Try frozen peaches for a colder texture.

- Add a basil leaf for a touch of sophistication.

Utensils needed:

- A blender

17. Detoxifying Green Tea Smoothie.

Begin your day with a cleansing combination of green tea, spinach, and tropical fruit. This smoothie not only benefits your liver, but it also delivers a modest energy boost.

Ingredients:

- 1 cup brewed green tea, cooled.

- One cup of pineapple pieces

- 1/2 peeled and sliced cucumber,

- 1 tablespoon honey, and 1 cup ice cubes.

Two servings.

Instructions:

1. In a blender, add cold green tea, pineapple chunks, cucumber slices, honey, and ice.
2. Blend until smooth and refreshing.
3. Strain into cups and enjoy the cool green tea infusion.

Features and Variations:

- Squeeze lemon for a zesty kick.

- If needed, add more honey to adjust the sweetness.

- Finish with a pineapple slice for a tropical touch.

Utensils needed:

- A blender

18. Carrot Orange Turmeric Elixir.

Enjoy the golden sweetness of this carrot, orange, and turmeric elixir. It's a colorful and zesty addition to your liver-friendly smoothie arsenal, jam-packed with immune-boosting nutrients.

Ingredient list:

- 1 cup peeled and sliced carrots.

- 1 cup orange segments.

- One teaspoon of turmeric powder.

- One spoonful of flaxseeds

- One cup orange juice.

Two servings.

Instructions:

1. Blend sliced carrots, orange segments, turmeric powder, flaxseeds, and orange juice.
2. Blend until smooth and bright orange.
3. Pour into glasses and enjoy the healthful elixir.

Features and Variations:

- Add a sprinkle of black pepper to improve turmeric absorption.

- Adjust the thickness as needed by adding additional orange juice.

- Add an orange slice as a final touch.

Utensils needed:

- A blender

19. Pomegranate Berry Burst.

Enjoy a blast of antioxidants with this pomegranate and berry smoothie. A wonderful combination of tastes that not only tantalizes the taste senses but also promotes liver health.

Ingredients:

- 1/2 cup pomegranate seeds

- 1 cup mixed berries (strawberries and blueberries)

- One-half banana

- One spoonful of chia seeds

- One cup of pomegranate juice

Two servings.

Procedure:

1. Blend pomegranate seeds, mixed berries, banana, chia seeds, and pomegranate juice.
2. Blend till smooth and full of berry delight.
3. Pour into glasses and enjoy the colorful medley.

Features and Variations:

- Add spinach for additional nutrients.

- Experiment with various berries to provide variation.

- Add pomegranate arils for a visually pleasing finish.

Utensils needed:

- A blender

20. Chocolate Avocado Dream.

This chocolate avocado dream smoothie will satisfy your sweet cravings while also benefiting your liver health. Creamy, chocolatey, and nutrient-dense—a guilt-free treat.

Ingredient list:

- 1 ripe avocado (peeled and pitted)
- 2 tablespoons cocoa powder.
- One-half banana
- One spoonful of almond butter.
- One cup almond milk.

Two servings.

Instructions:

1. Blend ripe avocado, cacao powder, banana, almond butter, and almond milk.
2. Blend until it's smooth and lovely.
3. Pour into glasses and enjoy the chocolatey avocado delight.

Features and Variations:

- Add a dash of vanilla extract for more taste.

- If desired, adjust the sweetness with a small amount of maple syrup.

- Add a sprinkling of cacao nibs for a crispy texture.

Utensils needed:

- A blender

CONCLUSION

Finally, starting a healthy lifestyle with the Fatty Liver Diet Cookbook for Newly Diagnosed People is more than simply a dietary option; it is a transforming step toward managing and minimizing the obstacles offered by fatty liver disease. As we dug more into this specialist cuisine, it became clear that a well-curated diet is critical to the comprehensive care of this illness.

The value of dietary intervention cannot be emphasized in the context of fatty liver disease. The cookbook is a complete reference that gives consumers with not just recipes, but also a thorough grasp of the nutrients, amounts, and dietary patterns required to maintain liver function. The emphasis on full, unprocessed foods, lean proteins, and healthy fats is consistent with accepted medical advice, making it an invaluable resource for people navigating the intricacies of newly diagnosed fatty liver.

The Fatty Liver Diet Cookbook's approach is very user-friendly. The dishes are not only delicious, but they are also designed to be simple, taking into account the various difficulties that people may have while adjusting to a new dietary pattern. The use of commonly available components guarantees accessibility without compromising nutritious value. As a result, this cookbook is a useful tool for integrating liver-friendly foods into daily living, making the shift to a healthy diet more manageable for people dealing with a new diagnosis.

Furthermore, the cookbook's emphasis on customisation acknowledges the specific requirements of those with fatty liver disease. It offers a diverse range of recipes that appeal to a variety of nutritional choices, allowing people to personalize their meal plans to their own tastes and cultural preferences. This individualized approach not only improves adherence to dietary standards, but it also promotes a sense of autonomy and control over one's health journey.

Beyond the culinary side, the Fatty Liver Diet Cookbook discusses the psychological and emotional aspects of adjusting to a new eating regimen. It recognizes the difficulties that individuals may confront while redefining their relationship with food and provides practical advice and insights to help them manage these changes. By encouraging a positive and supportive mentality, the cookbook evolves into a comprehensive guide that goes beyond the kitchen, enabling a long-term approach to health management.

The cookbook's evidence-based suggestions inspire confidence. The recipes and dietary suggestions for fatty liver disease are based on scientific principles and professional insights, and they are consistent with proven medical knowledge. This scientific foundation not only boosts the cookbook's legitimacy, but also presents it as a helpful complement to medical treatments, resulting in a synergy between food choices and professional medical care.

As we continue our examination of the Fatty Liver Diet Cookbook for the Newly Diagnosed, it is critical to emphasize the larger consequences of eating a liver-friendly diet. Beyond the immediate impact on liver health, such dietary changes improve general well-being by promoting cardiovascular health, weight control, and metabolic balance. As a result, the cookbook acts as a catalyst for long-term lifestyle adjustments that go far beyond a specific diagnosis.

Education is essential in the management of fatty liver disease, and the cookbook excels in this area. It enables people to make educated decisions that align with their health objectives by making information about the nutritional value of various foods, cooking techniques, and dietary plans readily available. This teaching component is a key tool, allowing people to become active participants in their health management rather than passive users of information.

In essence, the Fatty Liver Diet Cookbook for Newly Diagnosed People is more than simply a collection of dishes; it is a road map for a revolutionary lifestyle change. The cookbook shines as a light of hope for people navigating the challenges of fatty liver disease, thanks to its combination of simplicity, individuality, scientific rigor, and educational depth. As people engage on the culinary adventure, they are not just changing their diets, but also adopting a holistic approach to health that includes body, mind, and spirit.